TREES, SHRUBS AND FLOWERS

TO KNOW

IN ONTARIO

SHEILA M. McKAY
PAUL M. CATLING

ILLUSTRATIONS BY BETSY GORDON

J. M. DENT & SONS (CANADA) LIMITED

ACKNOWLEDGMENTS

We have benefited from the helpful advice and valuable criticism of many botanists and naturalists. We are in particular debt to Prudence Whiddington for her editorial help. The dried plant collection and library facilities at the University of Toronto were an invaluable asset, and the production of this book would have been a much more laborious task had we not had access to this well-organized data base. We wish to acknowledge with thanks the courtesy of the curatorial staff of the University of Toronto's vascular plant herbarium, Dr. John W. Grear, Ms. Dale Hoy, and Mr. John Riley, in making these facilities available to us. We would like to thank Dr. W. G. Barker, Chairman of the Department of Botany and Genetics, and Dr. J. F. Alex of the Herbarium for the use of the facilities at the University of Guelph, and for invaluable advice and criticism, and Mr. Claude Renaud for his help with the glossary.

Printed and bound in Canada
by
The Alger Press Ltd.
Oshawa, Ont.

Table of Contents

Introduction 7

The Vegetation of Ontario 13

Coniferous Trees and Evergreens 25

Deciduous Trees 32

Small Trees or Shrubs 55

Shrubs 67

Vines 94

Common Wildflowers 99

Other Distinctive Plant Groups 177
    Sedges 178
    Grasses 180
    Grass-leaved Plants 182
    Aquatic Plants 183
    Arums 186
    Saprophytes and Parasites 187

Appendix 189
    Ferns and Fern Allies 190
    Edible Plants 194
    Poisonous Plants 195

Index 196
Glossary 208
Pictorial Glossary inside front and back covers

INTRODUCTION

Why should you be interested in trees, shrubs, and wildflowers? When we first took a course in plant classification at University we were given the answer to this question during our first lecture. Quoting from a great botanist, our professor explained that plants are about us everywhere, and that if we took the time to learn their names and something about them, we would not only appreciate the world around us more completely, but see a whole new world unfolding before us, and experience unending pleasure exploring it. This was and is true! However, our enjoyment of plants preceded a technical training in botany at University. At an early stage we were influenced by our contact with a few very enthusiastic naturalists who had gained a knowledge of the names of the local plants, where they were found, when they flowered, how their seeds were transported, and other interesting facts. These people were variously employed: a salesman, a business executive, an artist, a nurse, and all had learned about plants in the pursuit of a part-time hobby.

We have intended this book for the part-time naturalist. It is not a complete technical guide, only a beginning, but it will enable you, without botanical training, to identify and learn something about the most common and obvious plants that grow without cultivation in Ontario. Almost 450 plants are illustrated, and we have tried to include the most interesting facts about them in the hope that it will also serve teachers, park naturalists, and students as a useful source of information.

Where to Begin

There are more than 4000 species of plants in all Canada that grow without cultivation, and over half of them are found in Ontario. These figures are very rough, but make it clear that a complete knowledge of our flora is likely to be obtained only by hard-working professional botanists. In a more restricted geographical area, one of the southern counties, for example, we find some 1000 species growing without cultivation, while a township may have 400-700 species, and a small park, conservation area, or forest may have 150-300 species. Beginning with the dominant and obvious plants (the trees, shrubs, attractive wildflowers, and ubiquitous "weeds"), you can quickly develop a familiarity with the flora on a local basis.

Although we may have about 2500 species growing without cultivation in Ontario, many of these are either very restricted or rare. At least 500 are widespread, common, and/or conspicuous. This book treats the latter group — the plants that people most often encounter and want to know something about. Beginning in your own local area, whether it be the woods about the cottage, a city ravine, a vacant lot, or the cracks in the sidewalk on the way to work, you should be able to find a good many of the plants included here.

Coverage

Since we have not been able to include all the trees, shrubs, and flowers of Ontario in a pocket manual of this size, it is necessary to elaborate a little on the basis of our selection. We have tried to include all the larger plants. Almost all the Ontario trees are included, as well as almost all the major groups of shrubs. In choosing wildflowers and other herbs, we have given some preference to those species which are prevalent in the more populated areas of the province. No preference was based on habitats: we thought that it was just as important to include introduced roadside weeds as our native woodland species. In addition to the almost 450 species which are illustrated, about 100 more are mentioned in the text.

Only wild plants, or plants that grow in Ontario without special care from people (i.e. without cultivation) are included. For example, the Dandelion, which is included, flourishes here in a great variety of habitats without direct help from us and in spite of our efforts to eradicate it, but the Petunia, which is not included, is found only in gardens and could not exist here without our care and attention.

How to Use this Book

We have divided this book into nine main sections. In the first section, which discusses the flora of Ontario in general terms, the major floristic zones are indicated as well as the common native species in each zone. In addition, plants characteristic of certain habitats and soil types are listed. Reference to these lists will help in identification, since the species to be expected in a particular area or habitat are indicated.

Following "The Vegetation of Ontario" are the illustrated sections treating major groups of plants. Referring quickly to these sections to ascertain their general contents, it should be easy to decide in which section an unknown plant is likely to be found. Identification is made by comparing the "mystery plant" with the illustration, and noting any distinctive features mentioned in the text.

Larger mature plants may be classified as trees, shrubs, or vines. The vines that twine about or fasten themselves to various supports or trail along the ground are easily distinguished. However, smaller herbaceous vines (*Convolvulus, Fagopyrum, Polygonum*) may be found in the wildflower section. Some plants do not co-operate with people at all. Poison Ivy may be a tall climbing vine, a shrub to about 1 m high, or may appear as a herb with most of the woody portions growing underground!

The conifers and evergreens represent a relatively well-defined group, but in distinguishing between trees and shrubs we sometimes encounter difficulty. The average or maximum height has been used by some botanists to make the distinction, but there has always been disagreement about what this height should be. Certain borderline species, such as Flowering Dogwood, make the line of demarcation difficult to establish. The distinction between trees and shrubs is, of course, arbitrary. Young trees may appear to be shrubs when height alone is used. For this reason, the presence of a single well-defined stem has been added to the definition of a tree. Even this is not ideal, though, since borderline cases still exist, and under certain environmental conditions a tree may develop many stems and a low stature, making it, by definition, a shrub. This has happened with Red Maple and Red Oak near Sudbury, apparently as a result of an unusual combination of stresses including fire, sulphur dioxide fumigation, and soil destruction. For our purposes here, trees are usually over 4.6 m (15') tall and have one well-defined stem. All of those individuals and groups that are difficult to assign we have placed in their own class: "Small trees or shrubs", suggesting their intermediate nature.

It should not come as a surprise that the distinction between shrubs and herbs is also sometimes problematic. Shrubs have woody branches growing above the ground, which survive the winter. Some creeping shrubs such as the Running Strawberry Bush (*Euonymus obovatus*) do not look very shrub-like, but the green branches are woody and perennial (lasting from year to year). The Twinflower (*Linnaea borealis*) and the Bunchberry (*Cornus canadensis*) both have woody parts above the ground, but are anything but shrub-like in appearance. You will find these two in the wildflower section.

The wildflower section is divided up according to flower colour. Although this is one of the easiest ways of identifying plants, especially for the beginner, it is not ideal, because plants are not always flowering. For this reason, along with many of the flower illustrations, other parts of the plant are shown. Another difficulty related to organizing plants according to their flower colour is that some plant species exhibit a variety of flower colours. A Musk Mallow, for instance, may have either pink or white flowers. We have placed such plants within the colour grouping in which they are most commonly found. If you cannot find a certain plant listed in its flower colour category, check the other colours as well. Even if the "mystery plant" is not listed at all, you may find a near relative of it that will help you to track it down elsewhere (see under "Absolute Identification").

Occasionally it is difficult to decide upon the flower colour, since some flowers have a combination of different colours. If your unknown flower is multi-coloured, try to establish the predominant colour by viewing it from a distance. Sometimes colours are not distinct but merge, making determination difficult. Here we have included yellowish-green and purplish-green under green, mauve under pink, reddish-purple under red, orange-yellow under orange, and cream and greenish-white under white. But most decisions about colour will be readily made and will make identification much easier.

The section entitled "Other distinctive plant groups" is one you should check over regularly, since the plants treated there are not found elsewhere in the book and are so distinctive that to recognize them, at least at the group level, is a simple matter.

Finally, an Appendix contains some notes on edible plants and poisonous plants, subjects of essential interest to the field botanist. The more common ferns and fern allies are discussed here as well. They are so often encountered with other wild plants that a very brief mention of the most common species seemed desirable.

Names

Plants are assigned two kinds of names: common names and scientific names. There may be numerous common names referring to a single plant, different ones being used in different parts of the country. For instance, our Common Mullein is known by 139 other common names in the various parts of its range. However, to a scientist there is only one correct name for any plant species and this is its scientific Latin name, which consists of two parts: the first is the generic name that represents a distinct group of one or more species, while the second name is the species name or specific epithet. The Common Buttercup, also called Tall Buttercup or Bouton-d'or (all common names), is scientifically known as *Ranunculus acris* throughout the world. "*Ranunculus*", meaning little frog (since many members of the group are aquatic or semi-aquatic), refers to the group of Buttercups in general, whereas "*acris*", meaning acrid or bitter-tasting, refers to this particular introduced species of our fields and meadows. Another plant, the Twinleaf (*Jeffersonia diphylla*) was given its genus or generic name in honour of Thomas Jefferson, third president of the United States, while the specific epithet "*diphylla*" refers to the two leaves which occur at the top of each stalk. The genus name of the Twinflower (*Linnaea borealis*) commemorates Carl von Linné, known more widely as Carolus.Linnaeus, the father of botanical naming, who in 1753 published the first book standardizing the binomial system of scientific names. The specific epithet "*borealis*" refers to the northern or boreal distribution of this dainty plant. The name "*Trillium*" reminds us that our floral emblem (*Trillium grandiflorum*) is a lily, having its foliage and flowers in arrangements of three (*tri* = 3), while the specific name "*grandiflorum*" refers to its relatively large flowers. Since the scientific names are standardized and are often descriptive of the plant, professional botanists use these names instead of the common names. Here we have included both the one or two most frequently used common names as well as the scientific name.

Absolute Identification

While some plants, including many of those treated here, are distinctive and easily distinguishable from their close relatives, others are more difficult to recognize and cannot be identified with certainty on the basis of comparison with drawings alone. These must be determined by using "keys", a more technical method.

With the increasing importance of floristic inventories in various parts of our province, the difficulty of plant identification must not be oversimplified. As far as scientific surveys are concerned, this book can be a valuable aid, but because of its semi-popular nature should not be the sole basis of identity decisions. For some plants even the technical books are insufficient, and to identify them accurately, dried material must be sent to professional botanists specializing in the classification of a particularly difficult group. In addition to the Botany Departments in various universities across the province, the National Museum and the Department of Agriculture in Ottawa, as well as the Royal Ontario Museum in Toronto, have botanists on their staff with a knowledge of the local flora.

Additional Reference Sources

1 BOOKS

As your knowledge and interest increase, you will find that a single book is rarely sufficient, and it is very likely that a growing interest in the local flora will lead you to investigate other sources. Of the several books available that treat the Ontario flora, we recommend for completeness and general ease of use the three hard-bound volumes of Gleason's *The New Britton and Brown Illustrated Flora*. This book is also available as a manual, without illustrations. Fernald's edition of *Gray's Manual* is also popular. Part 1 of the *Michigan Flora*, by Voss, is useful for much of southern Ontario and is partially illustrated. Some other books, which treat certain groups within our region more completely, are also listed: for example, those by Alex and Switzer, Cody, and Soper and Heimburger. The textbooks by Lawrence and by Porter provide valuable insight into higher plant taxonomy. *The Naturalist's Guide to Ontario*, by Judd and Speirs, will help you locate some of the most interesting natural areas in various parts of the province. The works of Boivin and Scoggan contain the most up-to-date published listing of plants found in the different provinces of Canada, including Ontario, and these are of special value to the more advanced student, since references to scientific papers concerning the taxonomy of specific groups are provided. All these books are available in libraries and most can be either directly purchased or ordered from bookstores.

Alex, J.F. and C.M. Switzer. [1976]. Ontario weeds. Publication 505, Ontario Ministry of Agriculture and Food. [208] pp.

Boivin, B. 1966-7. Énumeration des plantes du Canada. Provancheria no. 6. Mémoires de l'Herbier Louis-Marie. Les presses de l'Université Laval, Québec. 425 pp.

Case, F.W. Jr. 1964. Orchids of the western Great Lakes region. Cranbrook Institute of Science. Bloomfield Hills, Michigan. 147 pp.

Cody, W.J. 1956. Ferns of the Ottawa district. Canada Department of Agriculture. 94 pp.

Fernald, M.L. 1950. Gray's manual of botany. 8th ed. American Book Co., New York. 1632 pp.

Gleason, H.A. 1968. The new Britton and Brown illustrated flora of the northeastern United States and adjacent Canada. 3 vol. Hafner Pub. Co. Inc., New York. Vol. 1 (482) pp.), vol. 2 (655 pp.), vol. 3 (595 pp.).

Gleason, H.A. and A. Cronquist. 1963. Manual of vascular plants of northeastern United States and adjacent Canada. Van Nostrand Co. Inc., New York. 810 pp.

Judd, W.W. and J.M. Speirs. 1964. A naturalist's guide to Ontario. University of Toronto Press. 210 pp.

Lawrence, G.H.M. 1951. Taxonomy of vascular plants. Macmillan, New York. 823 pp.

Porter, C.L. 1967. Taxonomy of flowering plants. W.H. Freeman and Co., San Francisco. 472 pp.

Pringle, J.S. 1967. The common Aster species of southern Ontario. Royal Botanical Gardens, Hamilton, Ontario. Technical Bulletin No. 2. 15 pp. (Several others are available.)

Scoggan, H.J. 1957. Flora of Manitoba. National Museum of Canada, Ottawa. Bulletin no. 140. Biology series 47. 619 pp.

Scoggan, H.J. 1978. The flora of Canada. National Museum of Natural Sciences, National Museums of Canada. vols. 1-4.

Soper, J.H. and M.L. Heimburger. 1961. 100 shrubs of Ontario. Dept. of Commerce and Development. Toronto, Ontario. 100 pp.

Voss, E.G. 1972. Michigan flora, part 1, Gymnosperms and monocots. Cranbrook Institute of Science and University of Michigan Herbarium. Bloomfield Hills, Michigan. 488 pp.

2 MAGAZINES AND JOURNALS

The following magazines or journals, available in most libraries or by subscription, contain articles, notes, and reviews relating to the Ontario flora.

The Canadian Field-Naturalist, published quarterly, and Trail and Landscape, published bi-monthly by the Ottawa Field Naturalists' Club, Box 3264, Postal Station C, Ottawa, Canada K1Y 4J5.

The Ontario Field Biologist, published semi-annually (not including special issues) by the Toronto Field Naturalists' Club.

The Ontario Naturalist, published quarterly by the Federation of Ontario Naturalists, Toronto.

THE VEGETATION OF ONTARIO

Vegetation History

The great Wisconsin ice sheet melted away in southern Ontario about 10 500 years ago and disappeared from northern Ontario about 6000 years ago. Our flora, then, is not very old, geologically speaking. Soon after the ice sheet disappeared, a climate that was much the same as the present climate developed, although it was not entirely stable. Plants moved in from non-glaciated areas. Different species have different mechanisms of dispersal and hence different rates of spread. The Great Lakes, although gradually decreasing in size, may have impeded the spread of some species. Although most plants probably moved in from the south, some appear to have come from the southeastern uplands and eastern coastal plain. Some of these spread all the way to Georgian Bay, while others (Pitch Pine, for example) remained confined to a small area of the extreme southeast. Studies of pollen assemblages in bogs and lake sediments suggest that about 5000 years ago the climate was somewhat warmer than it is now. This period, referred to as the "climatic optimum" or "hypsithermal interval", is also suggested by the occurrence of fossil pine trees to the north of their present-day northern limits. It is possible that the climate was drier during the climatic optimum as well, and perhaps it was during this period that the mid-western prairie vegetation moved into extreme southwestern Ontario.

Humans have also played a significant role in establishing the character of our flora, beginning on a relatively small scale with the Indians, who created extensive clearings. In addition, Indians increased the incidence of fires, which probably stimulated plants preferring open sunny sites. Very likely the native inhabitants transported the seeds of various species that were edible, along with others of presumed medicinal value. The Hurons even practised an extensive agriculture, utilizing corn, pumpkins, and squash. It appears that the Indians created a special habitat for some species of plants that were not directly cultivated, and even today we find a more or less distinctive flora about some of the places that were important Indian settlements.

The impact of the Indians on our vegetation was slight compared to the effect of the Europeans, who arrived during the 17th century and by 1850 had already significantly altered the flora. Extensive forests of Sugar Maple, Beech, and Hemlock were cut down, to be replaced by agricultural crops, leaving only scattered forest remnants here and there. Open oak woodlands with sunny glades ablaze with native wildflowers have become an urban sprawl. We still have examples of the original vegetation types left, but some have been seriously reduced to a small percentage of the area that they once occupied. Over the past few years there has been a growing awareness of the need to preserve examples of our native vegetation, and although some of our very restricted vegetation types and rare species are now well protected, others are not. The continuity of many native plants and vegetation types in Ontario will depend upon our interest in preserving them.

The Europeans not only reduced the native flora, but both consciously and unconsciously brought with them a large number of European species. Various weed seeds were brought to North America, probably accidentally mixed with the seeds of crop plants or in the ballast of ships. Certain plants, in addition to the major crop plants, were introduced intentionally, because they were attractive or had medicinal values. Some of these plants found the new environment to their liking, and were without competition in the new man-made habitats. Many introduced species have spread widely, become abundant, and are now well established in our flora.

Vegetation Zones

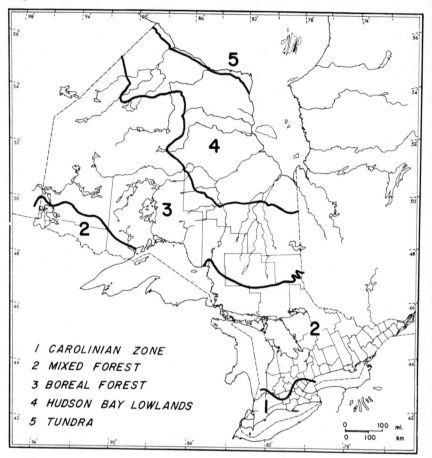

1 CAROLINIAN ZONE
2 MIXED FOREST
3 BOREAL FOREST
4 HUDSON BAY LOWLANDS
5 TUNDRA

Vegetation Zones

With a surface area of 940 900 km², Ontario spans about 15 degrees of latitude (about 1700 km). From east to west, the province includes almost 21 degrees of longitude (about 1600 km). Within so large an area it is not surprising to find a variety of climatic conditions.

It appears that climate is one of the predominant factors which control the distribution of the major vegetation zones. The Ontario climate is essentially continental, with relatively large annual temperature fluctuations and major seasonal contrasts. The summers are cool and short in the north but comparatively long in the extreme south. Rainfall is generally adequate for forest development, ranging from 660-1020 mm in parts of southern Ontario to 510-810 mm in parts of northern Ontario. The mean number of annual frost-free days ranges from 60-80 on the Hudson and James Bay coasts to over 180 in the Niagara Peninsula and Essex County regions.

These climatic variations result in a number of distinct vegetation types, from a subarctic tundra on the coast of Hudson Bay to the Carolinian forest in the Lake Erie region. Also referred to as the Deciduous Forest, the Carolinian forest covers much of the eastern United States, but has its northern limit in extreme southern Ontario. North of the Carolinian zone is the Mixed or Great Lakes - St. Lawrence Forest. Beyond this is the Boreal Forest region, and still further north a region of forest and barrens (muskeg), the Hudson Bay Lowlands, which eventually gives way to the narrow strip of coastal tundra.

1 THE CAROLINIAN (DECIDUOUS FOREST) ZONE

The forests of this zone consist mainly of broad-leaved trees that lose their leaves in the autumn (i.e. deciduous trees). In some places, high climbing vines such as Poison Ivy, Wild Grape, and Virginia Creeper are abundant. Evergreens and conifers such as White Pine, Tamarack, and Hemlock are scarce. Spruces are very rare and local. The characteristic trees, shrubs, and herbs are listed below. Those marked with two asterisks are confined to this zone in Ontario, and most of them are not found elsewhere in Canada. Those marked with one asterisk extend north of the Carolinian zone but remain confined to a small southern section of the Great Lakes - St. Lawrence forest.

Trees, shrubs, vines

Acer saccharum	** *Morus rubra*
* *Carya* spp.	** *Nyssa sylvatica*
* *Celtis occidentalis*	* *Parthenocissus inserta*
** *Cornus florida*	** *Platanus occidentalis*
* *Corylus americana*	* *Populus deltoides*
** *Euonymus obovatus*	** *Pyrus coronaria*
Fagus grandifolia	* *Quercus alba*
Fraxinus pennsylvanica	*Quercus borealis*
** *Gleditsia triacanthos*	** *Quercus palustris*
** *Gymnocladus dioica*	* *Quercus velutina*
* *Hamamelis virginiana*	* *Rhus radicans* var. *radicans*
* *Juglans cinerea*	* *Rhus vernix*
** *Juglans nigra*	** *Sassafras albidum*
* *Juniperus virginiana*	* *Staphylea trifoliata*
** *Liriodendron tulipifera*	*Tilia americana*
* *Lindera benzoin*	*Ulmus americana*
** *Maclura pomifera*	*Vitis riparia*
** *Magnolia acuminata*	* *Zanthoxylum americanum*
* *Menispermum canadense*	

Herbs

Allium tricoccum	*Erythronium americanum*
Anemone quinquefolia	*Geranium maculatum*
** *Arisaema dracontium*	*Hepatica acutiloba*
Asarum canadense	*Hepatica americana*
Caulophyllum thalictroides	* *Hydrophyllum appendiculatum*
* *Claytonia virginica*	* *Hydrophyllum canadense*
Dicentra cucullaria	* *Hydrophyllum virginianum*
* *Erythronium albidum*	* *Jeffersonia diphylla*

** *Mertensia virginiana*
* *Phlox divaricata*
* *Phytolacca americana*
Polygonatum pubescens
Podophyllum peltatum

Sanguinaria canadensis
Trillium grandiflorum
Uvularia grandiflora
* *Uvularia sessilifolia*

2 THE MIXED (GREAT LAKES - ST. LAWRENCE) FOREST ZONE

The forests of this region are of a mixed nature with both evergreens and deciduous species equally prominent over much of the area. There is much local variability, with some more northerly species such as Black Spruce, White Spruce, and Jack Pine, and eastern species such as Red Spruce, in certain areas. Species common in all or parts of this region are listed below. Those marked with an asterisk are rarely found in the Carolinian zone.

Trees and shrubs

* *Abies balsamea*
* *Acer pensylvanicum*
Acer rubrum
Acer saccharum
Acer spicatum
Betula lutea
Betula papyrifera
Corylus cornuta
Diervilla lonicera
Fagus grandifolia
Fraxinus americana
Lonicera canadensis
* *Nemopanthus mucronata*
* *Picea glauca*
* *Picea mariana*
* *Picea rubens*

Pinus resinosa
Pinus strobus
Populus balsamifera
Populus tremuloides
Prunus virginiana
Quercus borealis
Sambucus canadensis
Sambucus pubens
Spiraea alba
Spiraea latifolia
Taxus canadensis
Thuja occidentalis
Tilia americana
Tsuga canadensis
Ulmus americana
* *Viburnum alnifolium*

Herbs

Actaea alba
Aralia nudicaulis
Arisaema triphyllum
Aster macrophyllus
Botrychium virginianum
* *Claytonia caroliniana*
* *Clintonia borealis*
Coptis groenlandica
* *Cornus canadensis*
Erythronium americanum
Hepatica americana
* *Linnaea borealis*
Lycopodium spp.
Maianthemum canadense
Mitchella repens

Moneses uniflora
Osmorhiza claytoni
* *Oxalis montana*
Polygonatum pubescens
Pyrola elliptica
Smilacina racemosa
Solidago flexicaulis
Tiarella cordifolia
Trientalis borealis
Trillium cernuum
Trillium erectum
Trillium grandiflorum
* *Trillium undulatum*
Waldsteinia fragarioides

3 THE BOREAL FOREST ZONE

The Boreal Forest region is dominated by conifers, including Black Spruce, White Spruce, Balsam Fir, Tamarack, and Jack Pine. The few broad-leaved deciduous species prevalent here include White Birch, Trembling Aspen, and Balsam Poplar. Mosses are abundant and diverse on the forest floor. Extensive peatlands are found in some poorly drained areas such as the Clay Belt, and here the vegetation is mainly Black Spruce, sphagnum mosses, and shrubs of the Heath family. The northern limit of this zone corresponds approximately to the northern limit of the Canadian Shield uplands.

Trees and shrubs

Abies balsamea
Acer spicatum
Alnus crispa
Alnus rugosa
Amelanchier bartramiana
Betula papyrifera
Cornus stolonifera
Diervilla lonicera
Gaultheria hispidula
Kalmia angustifolia
Larix laricina
Ledum groenlandicum
Lonicera involucrata

Picea glauca
Picea mariana
Pinus banksiana
Populus balsamifera
Populus tremuloides
Prunus pensylvanica
Rubus acaulis
Rubus chamaemorus
Sorbus americana
Sorbus decora
Vaccinium myrtilloides
Viburnum edule

Herbs

Anemone quinquefolia
Aralia nudicaulis
Aster macrophyllus
Clintonia borealis
Coptis trifolia
Cornus canadensis
Epilobium angustifolium
Linnaea borealis
Maianthemum canadense

Mertensia paniculata
Mitella nuda
Moneses uniflora
Orthilia secunda
Potentilla tridentata
Pyrola asarifolia
Pyrola elliptica
Trientalis borealis
Viola renifolia

4 THE HUDSON BAY LOWLANDS (FOREST AND BARREN) ZONE

This is one of the few areas of the world where bogs and fens form a more or less continuous "sea". The area is essentially flat, sloping gradually (about 0.75 m/km) to the north. Fens consisting mainly of sedges occur where there is a flow of water, but where the water is stagnant, bogs develop, and in these, sphagnum moss, heath shrubs, and Black Spruce predominate. Black Spruce forest and spruce-lichen forests are found on drier sites. "Fingers" of boreal forest vegetation extend into this region along the banks of the major rivers that drain north into Hudson and James Bay. (For more detailed descriptions of this region see articles by Sjörs.)

Trees and shrubs	*Andromeda polifolia*	*Picea mariana*
	Betula pumila var. *glandulifera*	*Potentilla fruticosa*
	Chamaedaphne calyculata	*Rubus acaulis*
	Kalmia polifolia	*Salix* spp.
	Larix laricina	*Vaccinium oxycoccus*
	Ledum groenlandicum	*Vaccinium uliginosum*
	Myrica gale	
Herbs	*Calla palustris*	*Menyanthes trifoliata*
	Carex spp.	*Scirpus cespitosa*
	Drosera spp.	*Smilacina trifolia*
	Eriophorum vaginatum	
	and others	

5 THE TUNDRA ZONE

This narrow strip of vegetation along the Hudson Bay shore represents some of the southernmost sea-level tundra in the world. Probably maintained by cold air and sea fogs from Hudson Bay, it extends along the James Bay coast as well. Tundra is most extensive and reaches its best development at Cape Henrietta Maria. The coastal strip (including James Bay) has the only natural salt-marsh vegetation in the province. This region is rich in plant species, but due to its isolation and relatively restricted area, few of these have been treated in this book. Some of the more obvious plants are listed below. Anyone fortunate enough to travel into this most interesting zone will find the work of Porsild (1964) and Schofield (1959) particularly useful.

Arctostaphylos alpina	*Mertensia maritima*
Arenaria peploides	*Pedicularis* spp.
Arenaria rubella	*Polygonum viviparum*
Armeria maritima	*Rubus chamaemorus*
Carex scirpoidea	*Salix reticulata*
and others	and others
Dryas integrifolia	*Saxifraga tricuspidata*
Elymus arenarius	*Senecio congestus*
Empetrum nigrum	*Solidago multiradiata*
Hedysarum mackenzii	*Tofieldia pusilla*
Ledum decumbens	*Vaccinium uliginosum*
Ledum groenlandicum	*Vaccinium vitis-idaea*

Although no attempt is made here to describe the main vegetation zones in detail, it should be remembered that each major zone is itself a complex of subzones (sections), each with a distinct assemblage of plant species.

The southern Georgian Bay region, the Kingston region, and to a lesser extent the Ottawa Valley are areas of concentrations of southern species outside the Carolinian zone. The Algonquin highlands extending south to Bancroft have a greater floristic affinity with the Boreal region than do the other eastern parts of the Mixed Forest. A greater variety of factors, notably the local climate, topography, and nature of the substrate, determine the composition of these sections.

Habitats

A plant habitat is an area with particular environmental features in which a certain plant or group of plants occur. Knowing what plants to expect in certain habitats helps in identification and in understanding plant ecology. Some of the plants of natural woodland habitats in the major vegetation zones have already been listed. We will now consider very briefly some of the other kinds of habitats. Even this cursory survey will give some further insight into the reasons why certain plants occur in certain areas, and may help to explain some interesting distribution patterns.

1 WETLANDS

Wetlands are areas where there is surface water, or at least where it is wet underfoot for much of the year. They are dominant in the Hudson Bay Lowlands and characteristic of the Canadian Shield region, extending into the northerly parts of southern Ontario, whereas they are more localized further south in the province.

Five kinds of wetlands are recognized. (1) Bogs have acid, more or less stagnant, water and are characterized by sphagnum mosses and shrubs of the Heath family. (2) Fens have neutral or alkaline (and often slowly flowing) water, and are dominated by sedges, with sphagnum moss being very local or absent. Both bogs and fens are characterized by a scarcity of certain elements essential to the growth of plants, and the plants found in these wetlands are especially adapted to cope with a relatively low nutrient supply. Some obtain nutrients through the capture and digestion of insects, while others have evolved an ability to make do with relatively little. (3) Marshes, which normally have a good nutrient supply, are dominated by plants such as grasses, sedges, and cattails. (4) Swamps are forested wetlands where the water table is at or near the surface and standing water occurs during at least part of the year. Nutrients are usually in good supply. (5) Areas of more or less permanent shallow open water have floating and submerged aquatic plants.

Sometimes we find the various types of wetlands grading into one another or mixed to some extent, but generally they are distinctive and each type has a characteristic group of plants.

In areas of irregular topography resulting in impeded drainage, bogs are common. Outside the Shield region, southern Ontario's landscape is essentially flat, except for the escarpments and hilly glacial deposits called moraines. In the moraine areas, the topography is irregular and conditions of impeded drainage have led to the development of bogs. Bog plants that are common in the Shield region, but rare elsewhere in southern Ontario, may be found in hilly moraine country.

In the following list of wetland plants, those marked with an asterisk are bog species. Floating and submerged aquatics, often without flowers, are treated under "Other Distinctive Plant Groups".

Trees and shrubs		
	Acer rubrum	*Larix laricina*
	* *Alnus rugosa*	* *Ledum groenlandicum*
	* *Andromeda glaucophylla*	* *Myrica gale*
	* *Betula pumila* var. *glandulifera*	* *Nemopanthus mucronata*
	Cephalanthus occidentalis	* *Picea mariana*
	* *Chamaedaphne calyculata*	*Pinus strobus*
	Fraxinus nigra	*Salix* spp.
	Fraxinus pennsylvanica	*Thuja occidentalis*
	* *Ilex verticillata*	*Ulmus americana*
	* *Kalmia angustifolia*	* *Vaccinium angustifolium*
	* *Kalmia polifolia*	

Herbs		
	Alisma plantago-aquatica	*Lycopus americanus*
	Aster puniceus	*Lysimachia ciliata*
	Aster umbellatus	*Lythrum salicaria*
	Bidens cernua	* *Menyanthes trifoliata*
	Calamagrostis canadensis	*Mimulus ringens*
	Calla palustris	*Myosotis laxa*
	* *Calopogon tuberosus*	*Nuphar variegatum*
	Caltha palustris	*Platanthera hyperborea*
	Carex aquatilis	* *Pogonia ophioglossoides*
	Chelone glabra	*Pontederia cordata*
	Cicuta maculata	*Sagittaria latifolia*
	Conium maculatum	* *Sarracenia purpurea*
	* *Cypripedium acaule*	*Scutellaria galericulata*
	* *Drosera rotundifolia*	*Sium suave*
	Eupatorium maculatum	* *Smilacina trifolia*
	Eupatorium perforatum	*Solidago graminifolia*
	Gentiana andrewsii	*Solidago rugosa*
	Impatiens capensis	*Sparganium eurycarpum*
	Iris versicolor	*Typha latifolia*
	Lathyrus palustris	*Utricularia vulgaris*
	Lobelia cardinalis	*Verbena urticifolia*
	Lobelia siphilitica	

2 ACID AND ALKALINE HABITATS

The rare and local occurrence of certain acid-bog species in southern Ontario outside the Canadian Shield region has already been discussed. There are, in addition, a number of species with a distinct preference for drier acid soils. These plants are characteristic of the Shield region, where acid substrates are predominant, but they also extend locally to the south and east on sandy soils, which are generally acid in southern Ontario except in the immediate vicinity of the Great Lakes shores. Sand plains and moraine areas usually contain abundant drier acid sites. Plants characteristic of such habitats include: *Cypripedium acaule, Epigaea repens, Gaultheria procumbens, Hepatica americana, Lobelia inflata, Medeola virginiana, Monotropa uniflora, Myrica asplenifolia, Pinus strobus, Quercus borealis* and *Vaccinium angustifolium*.

Substrate and Landscape Features of Southern Ontario

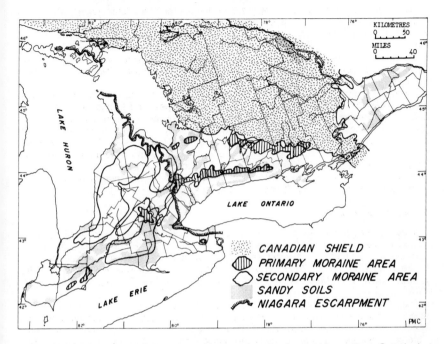

CANADIAN SHIELD
PRIMARY MORAINE AREA
SECONDARY MORAINE AREA
SANDY SOILS
NIAGARA ESCARPMENT

A relatively large group of plants are widespread and/or frequent in southern Ontario, but are either absent or very rare on the Canadian Shield. Some of these plants prefer alkaline substrates such as clay soils or the limestone rocks along the Niagara Escarpment. However, other factors such as the availability of open rocky habitats, topography, and even some climatic features also have limits that approximate the southern limits of the Shield region, so for many plants it is difficult to establish soil type as a single controlling factor. Plants that are widespread in southern Ontario outside the Shield region include the following:

Allium tricoccum	*Panax quinquefolia*
Castilleja coccinea	*Pedicularis canadensis*
Celastrus scandens	*Phlox divaricata*
Claytonia caroliniana	*Podophyllum peltatum*
Dentaria laciniata	*Quercus macrocarpa*
Eupatorium rugosum	*Rhamnus alnifolia*
Hepatica acutiloba	*Rhus aromatica*
Hydrophyllum virginianum	*Ribes americanum*
Juglans cinerea	*Salix candida*
Lobelia siphilitica	*Ulmus thomasi*
Menispermum canadense	*Viburnum rafinesquianum*

3 SHORES OF THE GREAT LAKES

Certain plants are distributed primarily around the shores of the Great Lakes, where they grow on dry sand dunes and in moist shoreline meadows (Guire and Voss, 1963). Presqu'ile, Long Point, Rondeau, and Pinery Provincial Parks all contain elements of a typical shoreline vegetation. Characteristic species include: *Arctostaphylos uva-ursi*, *Equisetum variegatum*, *Gerardia* spp., *Gentianella crinita*, *Juniperus* spp., *Liatris* spp., *Lithospermum caroliniense*, *Lobelia kalmii*, *Parnassia glauca*, *Prunus pumila*, and *Spiranthes cernua*.

Shorelines often provide a moderate or relatively cool microclimate, as well as continuous opportunities for colonization due to erosion, steep slopes, and fluctuating water levels. Such environmental conditions are not found inland except occasionally in deep river gorges. As a consequence, some species with essentially boreal affinity extend south only along shorelines and in deep gorges. A good example is the Bird's-eye Primrose (*Primula mistassinica*), which occurs along the shores of Bruce County and in the gorge of the Grand River near the town of Elora. The shoreline of Lake Superior has a remarkable assortment of arctic-alpine species, some of which cannot be seen elsewhere in Ontario except along the tundra shores of Hudson Bay (Soper and Maycock, 1963).

4 MAN-MADE HABITATS

Our natural woodlands, stream banks, prairies, and wetlands are dominated by native Canadian plants. Relatively few of the plants introduced from Europe have been able to compete with our native species in these natural habitats. Among the few that are able to do so are: *Alliaria officinalis*, *Chelidonium majus*, *Epipactis helleborine*, *Hesperis matronalis*, *Leonurus cardiaca*, *Rhamnus frangula*, *Rhamnus cathartica*, *Saponaria officinalis* and *Tussilago farfara*.

The situation in man-made habitats is very different. In vacant lots, along roadsides, railways, and pathways, and in pasture lands, we find that most of the plants are introduced species. About 75% of these aliens are European. Some notable exceptions are the Common Milkweed (*Asclepias syriaca*) and Canada Goldenrod (*Solidago canadensis*), both of which are native Ontario plants, and Ragweed (*Ambrosia* spp.) which appears to have moved into Ontario from the west during the 19th century.

Although most of our successful introduced species are herbs, some trees and shrubs occur in this group. Notable examples are *Ailanthus altissima*, *Berberis vulgaris*, *Caragana arborescens*, *Ligustrum vulgare*, *Lonicera tatarica*, *Rhamnus cathartica*, *Rhamnus frangula*, and *Syringa vulgaris*. Some of the characteristic plants of man-made habitats are listed below.

Wastelands, Vacant Lots, and Recently Disturbed Ground

Acer negundo	*Nepeta cataria*
Ailanthus altissima	*Oenothera biennis*
Ambrosia artemisiifolia	*Oxalis europaea*
Atriplex patula	*Polygonum aviculare*
Cerastium vulgatum	*Salsola kali*
Chenopodium album	*Setaria viridis*
Erigeron philadelphicus	*Stelleria media*
Malva neglecta	*Sisymbrium altissimum*
Melilotus alba	*Sonchus* spp.
Melilotus officinalis	

Lawns	Agropyron repens	Plantago major
	Capsella bursa-pastoris	Poa annua
	Cerastium vulgatum	Polygonum aviculare
	Digitaria spp.	Potentilla argentea
	Glechoma hederacea	Stellaria media
	Medicago lupulina	Taraxacum officinale
	Oxalis europaea	Trifolium repens
	Plantago lanceolata	

Roadsides	Agropyron repens	Malva moschata
	Anaphalis margaritacea	Medicago lupulina
	Asclepias syriaca	Medicago sativa
	Barbarea vulgaris	Melilotus alba
	Capsella bursa-pastoris	Melilotus officinalis
	Carduus nutans	Oenothera biennis
	Chrysanthemum leucanthemum	Phleum pratense
	Cichorium intybus	Plantago major
	Cirsium arvense	Poa pratensis
	Cirsium vulgare	Polygonum aviculare
	Dactylis glomerata	Prunella vulgaris
	Echium vulgare	Rumex crispus
	Epilobium angustifolium	Saponaria officinalis
	Erysimum cheiranthoides	Setaria viridis
	Hemerocallis fulva	Taraxacum officinale
	Linaria vulgaris	Tragopogon pratense
	Lotus corniculatus	Verbascum thapsus

Old Fields	Agropyron repens	Hypericum perforatum
	Amelanchier spp.	Mentha arvensis
	Aster ericoides	Phleum pratense
	Aster novae-angliae	Poa pratensis
	Cirsium arvense	Prunella vulgaris
	Cornus spp.	Ranunculus acris
	Crataegus spp.	Rhus typhina
	Dactylis glomerata	Solidago canadensis
	Daucus carota	Trifolium pratense
	Hieracium aurantiacum	Vicia cracca
	Hieracium florentinum	Vincetoxicum medium
	Hieracium floribunda	

ONTARIO VEGETATION REFERENCES

Guire, K.E. and E.G. Voss. 1963. Distributions of distinctive shoreline plants in the Great Lakes region. Michigan Botanist, 2(4): 99-114.

Jeglum, J.K., A.N. Boissonneau, and V.F. Haavisto. 1974. Toward a wetland classification for Ontario. Canadian Forestry Service, Dept. of the Environment information report 0-X-215. 54 pp. + appendices.

Maycock, P.F. 1963. The phytosociology of the deciduous forests of extreme southern Ontario. Canadian Journal of Botany 41: 379-438.

Porsild, A.E. 1964. Illustrated flora of the Canadian Arctic Archipelago. National Museum of Canada. Bulletin No. 146. 218 pp.

Rowe, J.S. 1972. Forest Regions of Canada. Dept. of the Environment. Canadian Forestry Service Publication 1300.

Scoggan, H.J. 1959. The native flora of Churchill, Manitoba. National Museum of Canada. Ottawa. 51 pp.

Sjörs, H. 1959. Bogs and fens in the Hudson Bay lowlands. Arctic, 12(1): 3-19.

Soper, J.H. 1962. Some genera of restricted range in the Carolinian flora of Canada. Transactions of the Royal Canadian Institute 34(1): 1-56.

Soper, J.H. and P.F. Maycock. 1963. A community of arctic-alpine plants on the east shore of Lake Superior. Canadian Journal of Botany 41: 183-198.

Coniferous Trees and Evergreens

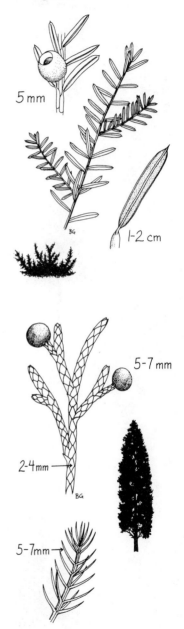

AMERICAN YEW
(Taxus canadensis)

This low spreading shrub of the forest floor occurs mainly in damp shaded woodlands. Because the branches parallel the ground before curving upward, a saucer-shaped colony develops, which is usually about 1 m high. The flat needles are individually attached in a spiral arrangement on the twigs, but their stalks are twisted so that the branch appears as a flat spray. The sharp-pointed uniformly green needles distinguish Yew from young Hemlock and Balsam Fir, which have prominent white lines beneath and blunt tips. Although evergreen, this species and the next do not bear cones, but produce fleshy berry-like fruits which are eaten by many species of birds. In mid to late summer the orange-red cup-shaped "berry" contrasts with the dark-green foliage. Widespread in Ontario, Yew is characteristic of the Mixed Forest region.

EASTERN RED CEDAR
(Juniperus virginiana)

The ascending bluish-green branches produce the distinctive columnar form of this tree. As it matures, the crown becomes more open and irregular. Rarely growing to over 10 m in height, Red Cedar usually colonizes rocky and gravelly ridges, and does best on alkaline soils. It occurs sporadically along the L. Erie and L. Huron shores, is frequent in the eastern L. Ontario region, spreads north to the Ottawa valley, and occurs irregularly along the southern limit of the Canadian Shield. The young shoots have slender sharp-pointed needles, and the older ones have scale-like needles forming four-sided branchlets. The female and male "cones" occur on different trees. One or two seeds are produced in the dark-bluish berry-like fruits, which are about the size of a pea and have a whitish bloom. The deep reddish fragrant heartwood of these cedars is often used for making chests and lining closets.

Common Juniper (*J. communis*) has needle-like spine-tipped leaves arranged in 3s and varies from 0.5-2 m in height, whereas Creeping Juniper (*J. horizontalis*) has spreading branches that trail over the ground. Both occur on rocky or sandy lakeshores, although the former is more widespread.

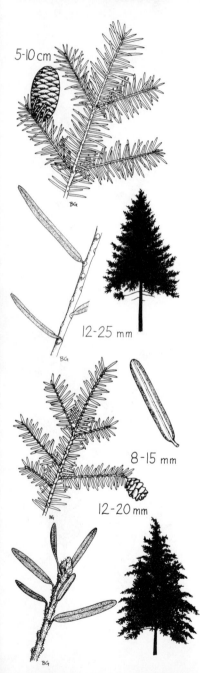

BALSAM FIR
(Abies balsamea)

Firs are small to medium-sized trees with dense, tapering, spire-like crowns, and branches which come off the main trunk in distinct planes or whorls, resulting in the typical Christmas-tree shape. Fir needles, unlike those of the Yews, are not sharp-pointed and they have white lines beneath. The leaves and branches are similar to those of Hemlock, except that the individual needles are not stalked, and when lost leave a distinctive circular scar on the twig. Firs have rather large female cones, which differ from those of other conifers in standing erect on the branches. They turn from violet to brown and by autumn the scales fall away, leaving a naked spike. The characteristic blisters on the trunks of young trees contain a clear resin which is the source of Canada Balsam, a glass cement for optical instruments. Typically a Boreal Forest species, Fir is most frequent and widespread in the north. The soft wood is important in the pulp and paper industry. Firs are often used as Christmas trees, since they hold their needles longer than spruces and are so pleasantly fragrant.

EASTERN HEMLOCK
(Tsuga canadensis)

Delicate spreading foliage which appears bright green above and silvery beneath characterizes this species. Unlike the pines, firs, and spruces, all with their strong upright leader shoots, Hemlock has a drooping terminal shoot which generally points away from the prevailing wind direction and forms a natural compass. The flat leaves are attached singly on short slender stalks to the hairy twigs and appear to be in a horizontal plane, have distinctive round tips, and white lines below. The male and female cones develop at the ends of the preceding year's branchlets. The pendant female cones turn from pink to brown and harden, releasing winged seeds during the first winter, but unlike fir cones they remain intact. This tree of the Mixed Forest occurs either in pure stands or with Yellow Birch, Sugar Maple, or Beech, usually in moist hilly woods. Once used by the Indians to dress wounds, the inner bark is today used in tanning leather.

TAMARACK ✓
(Larix laricina)

Although a conifer, tamarack is not an evergreen, for in late autumn the light bluish-green needles turn a bright golden yellow and are shed. The trees are tall and slender with a narrow open crown of many irregularly arranged horizontal branches. The flexible needles are borne singly on thin elongated twigs or appear in clusters of 10 to 20 on short spur shoots. Tamarack is a tree of cold, wet, poorly drained sites and grows to the northern limit of trees in Ontario within a few miles of the Hudson Bay shore; but it can also grow on better-drained areas in the north, where it is often present with Trembling Aspen, White Birch, and Balsam Fir. In southern Ontario it occurs only in cold bogs and fens, usually with Black Spruce and Cedar. Since the wood is very heavy, hard, and strong, and is very durable when in contact with soil, it is often used for fence posts, telegraph poles, and railway ties.

1-2 cm

EASTERN WHITE CEDAR
(Thuja occidentalis)

The yellowish-green pyramidal growth of this species, with branches reaching nearly to the ground, are key features to check for. Look closely to see the two types of small scale-like leaves, which give a jointed appearance to the branchlets. Also notice the small upright cones, which have pointed opposite scales. The female cones mature by late summer, and the seeds are shed the following year. Although this tree can grow in a great many habitats from swamps to stream banks or dry rocky ridges, it always does best on alkaline soil. Occurring throughout southern Ontario and extending to southern James Bay, it grows either in pure stands or mixed with other species. It is often associated with an early stage in forest development. The soft light wood is highly durable and easily split. The Indians used cedar to make the ribs, thwarts, and gunwales of their canoes. Early white settlers constructed a great variety of split-rail ("snake") fences from cedar. These fences and the cedar shingles on older farm buildings may still be seen in various parts of the province.

12 mm

(27)

PINES

You can easily identify pines by their long needle-shaped leaves, which are grouped together in clusters (fascicles) of from 2 to 5. The male cones, which produce the pollen, last for only a few weeks in the spring, but the female cones persist, becoming hard and woody as they mature. In most other conifers the winged seeds ripen in one season, but it takes pine seeds at least 2 years to mature.

EASTERN WHITE PINE
(Pinus strobus)

The long bluish-green needles have a soft and flexible texture, and occur in clusters of 5. Since the branches come out in whorls from the growing tip each year, it is possible to count up the spaces between the whorls and estimate the age of young trees. Once the lower branches are lost you cannot be quite so sure of your accuracy — but it's fun to see if you are older than the tree or not. Occasionally reaching heights of 60-70 m with diameters of 2 m, White Pine is our tallest conifer and produces our most valuable softwood lumber. Not only did the first settlers build their log cabins and furniture from the durable but easily worked wood, but in the early 1800s lumbering of White Pine was the most important Canadian industry. Rafts of huge squared timbers were sent down the Ottawa River from forests along the Petawawa, Madawaska, and Bonnechère rivers to provide the much needed materials for the British shipbuilding industry. White Pine occurs throughout southern Ontario in mixed or coniferous forests, reaching its northern limit about 150 km north of Lake Superior.

JACK PINE
(Pinus banksiana)

The needles are stiff, occur in bundles of 2, and are shorter than those of our other pines. The curled cones often remain closed and persist on the tree for many years, sometimes becoming buried in the bark as the tree matures. The heat intensity of a forest fire opens the cone scales, releasing the seeds. This and the rapid colonization of Jack Pine on burned areas explains why ecologists speak of it as a "fire-adapted" species. Characteristic of the boreal forest, it often forms pure stands to 25 m tall. In southern Ontario it is planted in reforestation areas.

The introduced Scots Pine (*P. sylvestris*) has bright-orange twigs, and although the needles are in 2s, they are 3-7 cm long, bluish-green, and sharply pointed.

RED PINE
(Pinus resinosa)

This conifer is the one that is most commonly grown in reforestation plantations. It does not suffer from weevils or blister rust as much as White Pine, and grows straight and tall to 25 m, or even 40 m. It is absent from extreme southern Ontario, occurring most frequently in the Canadian Shield region. The long dark-green needles, which are in clusters of 2, are sharp-tipped, straight, and flexible, but will break cleanly when bent in half. The distinctive orange-red bark has a flaky appearance.

The Pitch Pine (*P. rigida*) also has relatively long needles, but is confined in Ontario to rocky outcrops near Kingston. The yellowish-green needles, in clusters of 3, are often twisted, have blunt tips, and are rather stiff. The tufts of short branches on the main stem produce an unkempt appearance. Open-grown trees, 10-15 m tall, are often contorted. This interesting species appears to be on the decline in our area.

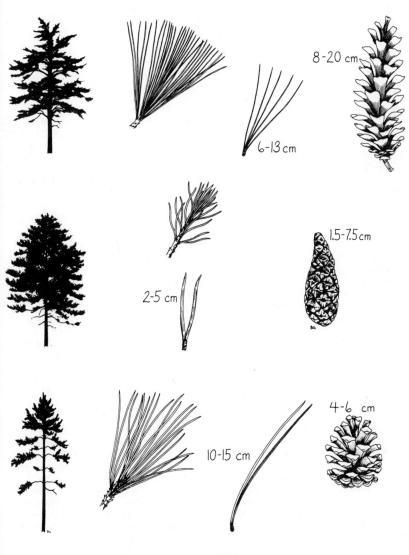

8-20 cm

6-13 cm

1.5-7.5 cm

2-5 cm

10-15 cm

4-6 cm

SPRUCES

Everyone knows the long pyramidal shape of a spruce. Note that the relatively short needles are raised on peg-like projections, which remain attached to the twig when the leaves are lost. Roll a four-sided needle between your thumb and forefinger. Spruce twigs usually have a close spiral of individual needles that form a cylindrical rather than a flattened branch. Spruces are not the best choice for Christmas trees despite their perfect shape, for they tend to lose their needles very rapidly when brought indoors. However, the light colour, low resin content, and long wood fibres make spruces the most important trees for the pulp and paper industry.

WHITE SPRUCE
(Picea glauca)

The uniform conical crown of White Spruce is a symbol of the north. Widely used in reforestation programs and in Christmas-tree plantations, this tree now occurs more commonly in southern Ontario, although under natural conditions it grows only in the Boreal and Mixed Forest regions, and sparingly southward. Its best growth is observed on well-drained but moist silty soils, especially along lake shores and stream banks, and on slopes. The needles are green to bluish-green but sometimes have a whitish bloom, and when crushed give off a strong odour. The twigs are pale brown to greyish and are without hairs. The roots when boiled are very pliable and were used by the Indians for lacing their birch-bark canoes and baskets. Today this species is mainly used for lumber and pulpwood.

BLACK SPRUCE
(Picea mariana)

The long straight trunk supports a narrow conical crown of short branches. The crown often becomes compact and dense in appearance, forming a slender pyramid, while the basal branches droop. The young twigs are covered with brownish hairs, a feature which readily distinguishes them from White Spruce. The needles are dark bluish-green with a whitish bloom, short and thick with blunt tips, and remain on the tree for 7 to 10 years. The small round female cones have ragged-edged scales and feel rough along the outer margin. A real Boreal Forest tree, Black Spruce occurs only in cold bogs in southern Ontario, but farther north it frequently grows on better-drained sandy loam soils. In bogs, when the lower branches become embedded in the sphagnum, they produce roots and form new trees, a phenomenon called layering. This is especially important in the far north where the trees grow very slowly and a 20- or 40-year-old "tree" might be only 1 m tall.

RED SPRUCE
(Picea rubens)

The broad columnar shape, yellowish-green shiny and often curved needles, as well as the orange-brown slightly hairy twigs, are distinctive features of Red Spruce. The narrow egg-shaped cones, which are pointed when closed, remain on the tree until the following summer and are much firmer than those of White Spruce. Red Spruce prefers moist sandy loam soils. An element of the East-coast or Acadian Forest, it occurs only in the east-central part of Ontario especially through the Algonquin Park-Haliburton-Bancroft area. Because of its resonant qualities, its wood is often used for the sounding boards of musical instruments. A renowned cure for scurvy, spruce beer was made by boiling the young twigs and leaves of Red or Black Spruce, adding molasses, honey, or maple sugar, and allowing the mixture to ferment.

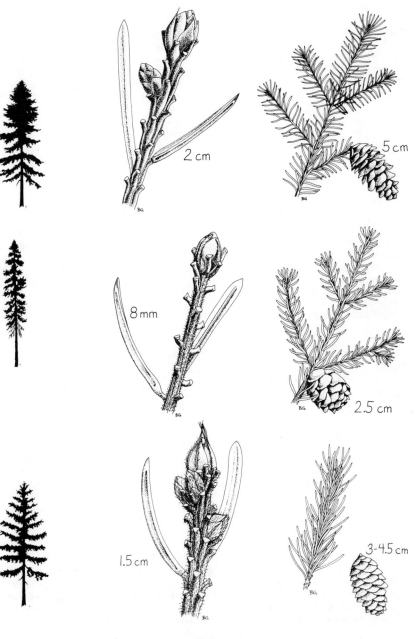

2 cm

5 cm

8 mm

2.5 cm

1.5 cm

3-4.5 cm

Deciduous Trees

POPLARS

These fast-growing short-lived trees have broad alternate leaves. As in willows, numerous small flowers occur in elongate clusters called "catkins", but in poplars the catkins are long and drooping instead of erect. Trees have either all male or all female catkins. Pollen is carried by the wind before the leaves unfold. Seeds occur in flask-shaped fruits and have tufts of silky hairs which aid in wind dispersal. The long-pointed buds have several overlapping scales. Poplars are important food for wildlife and favourite food of beavers.

WHITE POPLAR
(Populus alba)

This European tree, 15-25 m tall, has escaped from cultivation in many parts of southern Ontario. The thick leathery leaves are dark-green above and white woolly beneath, with only a few coarse teeth and from 3-5 lobes on the 5-13 cm blades. Rounded petioles as well as soft white hairs on the young twigs and buds are characteristic.

EASTERN COTTONWOOD
(Populus deltoides)

Broadly triangular leaves (6-13 cm wide) with 2-3 glands where the leaf joins the leaf stalk are distinctive features. The dark-grey bark has deep furrows. Long buds, 15-25 mm, are very sticky but not fragrant and curve away from the greenish or yellowish twigs. Cottonwood is one of our fastest-growing trees, young specimens increasing their height by about 2 m each year. Sometimes maximum height of 30 m is reached in 15 years. Found along river banks and lake shores and in bottom lands, Cottonwood is most common in the Carolinian zone, but extends north at least to Ottawa.

BALSAM POPLAR
(Populus balsamifera)

The finely toothed leaves, which appear bronzy-green above and pale below, are joined to the shiny reddish-brown twigs by a round petiole. The sticky resinous buds (15-25 mm) produce a strong fragrance in spring. Most common in northern Ontario, Balsam Poplar reaches 20-25 m tall and is frequent on gravels and moist soils along rivers.

TREMBLING ASPEN
(Populus tremuloides)

Golden yellow in fall, the nearly circular leaves, 2-7 cm long, are joined to the stem by a flattened petiole, making them unstable in the wind. The slightest breeze causes the foliage to rustle, and in several languages the common name translates as "woman's tongue". The bark is greyish-white to cream with dark warty patches. Twigs and small buds (5-7 mm) are shiny reddish-brown. Reaching 10-15 m tall, Trembling Aspen is often found in pure stands in dry open woods and recently burned areas. It occurs throughout much of Ontario, but is most common in the north.

LARGE-TOOTHED ASPEN
(Populus grandidentata)

This species, often reaching 15-25 m, has bark and an outline like those of the Trembling Aspen. It differs in having stouter twigs and buds that are greyish and downy, as well as leaves with fewer and larger rounded teeth. Found on dry hillsides, in woods, and along borders of streams, it occurs in the Carolinian and Mixed Forest regions.

(33)

CRACK WILLOW
(Salix fragilis)

Introduced from Europe as an ornamental, this tree with grey or greyish-brown deeply furrowed bark may become 25 m tall. In Crack Willow, the 2 stipules at the base of the leaf stalks are small and soon lost. The alternate leaves, 6-15 cm long, taper to the leaf stalk (where there are often 2 glands), and each tooth along the margin is tipped with a gland. The leaf under surface is much paler than the upper surface. The young twigs, finely hairy and reddish to yellowish brown, become a smooth shiny brown with age. They are very brittle at the base, and in a storm may snap off with a cracking sound. As in the other Willows, the buds are protected by a single cap-like bud scale. Flowering occurs early in the spring, before the leaves are fully expanded. Crack Willows bear either all male or all female catkins on one plant. Preferring moist ground, they are widespread in Ontario.

BLACK WILLOW
(Salix nigra)

Our largest native willow may be found in shrub or tree form, ranging in height from 3-20 m. The deeply furrowed trunk is dark brown or black. Finely toothed leaves have long-tapering points which are often curved at the very tip. They are rounded at the base where they join the short leaf stalk, without glands, and about the same shade of green on both sides. They may be up to 2 cm wide, whereas the leaves of Crack Willow are usually 2-4 cm wide. Heart-shaped stipules remain on the young shoots until the autumn. The young twigs vary from reddish-brown to pale orange. In May, the male and female catkins occur on different trees. Honey bees may depend on the pollen and nectar of these flowers for raising their spring broods. Later, the small fruits (less than 6 mm) split to release minute seeds with tufts of silky hairs which are carried by the wind. Black Willow is found in southern Ontario along stream banks and lake shores, and in swamps. Since it roots easily and is fast growing, branches are often planted on eroding river banks to stabilize the slopes.

WALNUTS

The compound leaves, with 7-23 toothed leaflets, are always alternate and glandless. In May and June, each tree has male flowers hanging in catkins, and female flowers in short spikes. The bony fruit has a fleshy outer covering around the seeds, which are sweet and edible. The pith of the twigs has many chamber-like partitions. Buds are large, thick, and usually white woolly. A chemical produced by the fruit husks of Walnuts discourages the growth of other plants beneath the trees, thereby decreasing competition for soil moisture and nutrients.

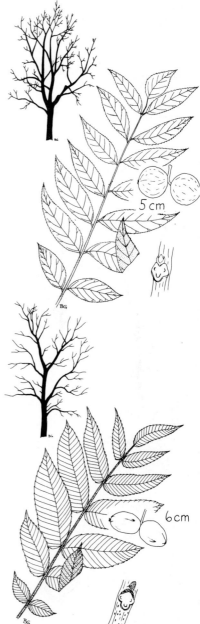

BLACK WALNUT
(*Juglans nigra*)

Diagnostic features include: an even number of broad-based leaflets or an odd number with a relatively small terminal leaflet; a spherical rather than an elongated fruit; a light-brown or buff pith in the twigs; large heart-shaped leaf scars with a notch at the top; and dark deeply grooved bark with dull rather than shiny ridges. Mostly confined to moist woods in the Carolinian zone, these trees grow 25-30 m tall, but large specimens are becoming increasingly scarce. This is one of our most valuable native trees. Its wood, which is heavy, strong, durable, and easily worked, is in great demand as a veneer.

BUTTERNUT
(*Juglans cinerea*)

Butternut differs from Black Walnut in always having odd numbers of leaflets, which are parallel-sided rather than broader at the base. The oblong fruits are sticky and hairy, and the pith of the twigs is dark brown. Triangular leaf scars have downy pads above them and are not notched. The bark is a light grey colour with flat ridges and darker crevices. Butternut trees, 15-20 m tall, are found sparingly in the Carolinian and southern Mixed Forest zones in dry rocky woods or well-drained rich bottom lands. The wood, which is light and soft, is not as valuable as that of Black Walnut. Sugar can be made from the sap in spring, and the green fruit husks may be used to dye cloth yellow or orange.

(35)

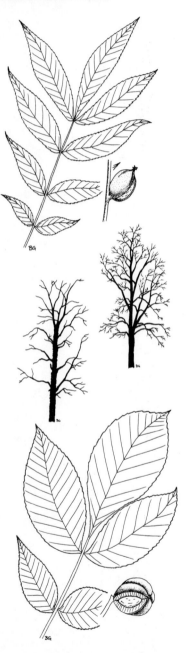

BITTERNUT HICKORY
(Carya cordiformis)

All hickories have alternate compound leaves with an uneven number of finely toothed leaflets. In May and early June, the male flowers occur on 3-branched catkins and the female flowers are in small clusters on the same tree. The 9 leaflets of Bitternut are narrower than those of other Ontario hickories. The gland-dotted sulphur-yellow buds aid in identification. Slender twigs are shiny greenish to greyish brown. At first smooth, the trunk later develops a tight wavy-lined bark. The round-ish fruits (2.5 cm long), which fall in early autumn, have thin 4-winged husks which, like those of the other Hickories, split into 4 segments revealing a 4-ridged nut-shell. Primarily a species of bottom lands and rocky limestone woods, it occurs in the Carolinian and southern Mixed Forest.

SHAGBARK HICKORY
(Carya ovata)

The dark-grey bark separates into long vertical strips that peel away at both the upper and lower ends, giving the trunk a shaggy appearance. The wide leaves usually have 5 leaflets, which are broadest above the middle. Fruits (2.5-3.5 cm) are broadly rounded, and the thick woody husk has 4 indentations. The heavy wood is hard, tough, and strong. Since it can withstand sudden shocks, such tools as axes are made from it. The Shagbark shares a similar distribution and grows in similar habitats as the Bitternut. Three less common hickories occur locally in the Carolinian zone. Also with shaggy bark, the Big Shellbark Hickory (*C. laciniosa*) usually has 7 leaflets which are velvety-brown beneath, and large fruits (5-6 cm) with a thick husk. Mockernut Hickory's (*C. tomentosa*) 7-9 leaflets are fragrant and woolly beneath, but its bark is tight with smooth ridges. Pignut Hickory (*C. glabra*) has thin fruit husks, green or brown buds (never yellow), broad leaflets, and pear-shaped fruits. The last two are dry upland species, while the first does best in moist valley bottoms. Except for the Pignut and Bitternut, the seeds of Hickories are edible; those of the Shagbark are sold commercially.

BIRCHES

The doubly toothed leaves are simple and alternate, but appear to be in pairs on older branches with dwarf shoots. The twigs typically zigzag. Tightly closed male catkins are conspicuous in winter, while the female catkins are enclosed in buds. Flowering occurs in spring before the foliage interferes with wind-carried pollen. Two-winged nutlets are later produced in cone-like catkins. Twigs, buds, and seeds are favourite winter foods of wildlife. Birch is an important source of lumber and pulpwood.

YELLOW BIRCH
(Betula lutea)

The thin bronze or yellowish bark peels back much like that of White Birch, but later coarse plate-like scales develop. Young twigs are greenish brown. The female "cones", which are held erect, disintegrate slowly during the winter, releasing the seeds. The leaves usually have 8 or more veins on each side. Yellow Birch reaching 20-25 m is found in cool moist sites in the Carolinian and Mixed Forest zones. Cherry Birch (*B. lenta*), which is confined in Ontario to the Niagara Peninsula, differs in having singly toothed leaves with heart-shaped instead of round bases, and black platy bark. Wintergreen can be distilled from the twigs of both species.

WHITE BIRCH
(Betula papyrifera)

The twigs, at first reddish-brown, later become smooth and creamy-white with thin strands of bark curling away like paper. Tearing off the bark often kills the tree. Leaves of White Birch have less than 8 veins on each side. The drooping female catkins are longer and more slender than those of Yellow Birch and are readily shed in the autumn. White Birch, reaching 15-25 m, occurs throughout much of Ontario. Indians made their canoes, tepees, and cooking utensils from the bark. Grey Birch (*B. populifera*), spreading into Ontario from farther east, has long-pointed triangular leaves. Able to grow on dry sterile soils, it often colonizes burned areas.

25-3mm

8 mm

4-6.5mm

4-5.5mm

(37)

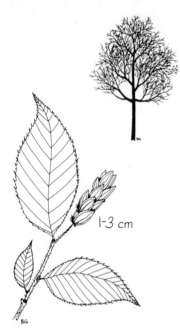

IRONWOOD
(Ostrya virginiana)

Primarily an understory tree, 6-10 m tall, Ironwood occurs in Carolinian and Mixed Forest woodlands. The doubly toothed leaves are birch-like, but have short stalks; they look similar to those of Blue Beech, but turn yellowish-green instead of red in the autumn. The narrow vertical strips of bark which peel off at both ends are a distinctive feature of Ironwood. Although the leaves might be confused with those of Elms, Birches, or Blue Beech, these species do not have shred-like bark. Flowers of Ironwood appear with the leaves in late April and May, the male catkins having been on the tree all winter, but the female catkins emerge from the buds. Drooping clusters of bladder-like pods, up to 5 cm long, fall during the winter. Inside each inflated sac (1-3 cm) is a nutlet (5 mm). The fruit looks similar to Hops, hence the common name Hop-hornbeam. The wood of this tree is so hard and strong that park naturalists sometimes find it easier to nail the sign identifying it to an adjacent tree.

AMERICAN BASSWOOD
(Tilia americana)

Basswood has heart-shaped leaves, up to 14 cm, with sharp teeth, uneven bases and long leaf stalks. Its creamy-yellow, 5-petalled flowers (1 cm across) open in July after the leaves are full grown. They are fragrant, and Basswood honey is produced from their nectar. A leaf-like blade, which supports the flowering and fruiting clusters, remains on the tree into winter and aids in the dispersal of the fruits, since it acts like a spinning parachute when it falls. The roundish nut-like fruit is about the size of a pea. The shiny zigzag twigs are yellowish brown and the buds dark red or greenish. Older bark is greyish brown, ridged, and scaly. There are usually a number of young sprouts growing from the base of the trunk. Basswood, reaching heights of 25 m, is found in rich woods in the Deciduous and Mixed Forest regions. The soft light wood is often used in carving. Indians made a strong tangle-free rope from the bark fibres.

(38)

AMERICAN BEECH
(Fagus grandifolia)

One of the dominant trees of the Deciduous and southern Mixed forests, Beech is most readily distinguished by its light bluish-grey, smooth bark. Buds are very long (2-2.5 cm) and slender. In late April and May, the male and female flowers open in separate circular clusters, after the leaves have unfolded. In the autumn the reddish-brown 4-parted husk, which is covered with weak spines, opens to release 2 triangular beechnuts. The leaves are at first thin and papery, but later become thicker and more leathery. In autumn they turn yellow and often remain on young trees through winter. Since the leaves are resilient and do not mat easily, the settlers sometimes used them to stuff mattresses. The edible nuts are a favourite food of Black Bears, which leave claw marks in the smooth bark while climbing the trees. These marks expand as the tree increases in thickness, leading to exaggerated stories about "giant bears".

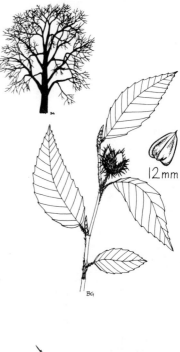

Beech reaches 25 m in height and usually grows on well-drained slopes and rich bottom lands, with Sugar Maple and Eastern Hemlock. In our area these slow-growing trees are called the "climax" forest species. They come to dominate the forest because their own seedlings are the most successful in deeply shaded conditions. The forest composition thus remains unchanged. Fires or other disturbances that destroy this forest result in the colonization of fast-growing, short-lived trees, and a series of successional stages finally restores a Beech-Maple-Hemlock climax. (See also Blue Beech, p. 59.)

SWEET CHESTNUT
(Castanea dentata)

This Carolinian species of sandy soils has leaves which are similar to those of the Beech, but are longer and narrower. The ridged bark, as well as the long and thin male catkins, the very spiny bur-like husks around the nuts, and the small oval buds are also distinctive. Sweet Chestnuts reaching 30 m tall used to be frequent in our southern Ontario forests until the 1920s, when most trees were killed by a fungal blight which spread from Asian plants imported into the U.S.A. Fruit-bearing specimens are now very rare in Ontario.

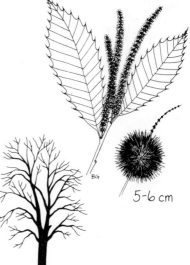

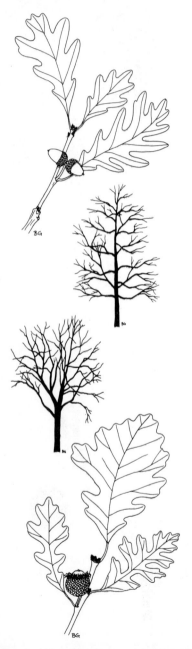

OAKS

All oaks have simple, alternate, toothed or lobed leaves, and acorns which are thin-shelled nuts set in a cup of overlapping scales. They are among the latest trees to produce leaves in spring and the last to drop their leaves in autumn. Usually flowers of both sexes open on the same tree while the leaves are unfolding in late May or early June. Long male catkins occur in clusters, and the small female flowers may be either solitary or grouped together in clusters of a few flowers each. The remarkable "oak apples" are large round swellings that are produced on the leaves of some oaks in response to insect (gall fly) attack. The hard strong wood is much in demand for furniture and flooring.

White Oak Group — leaves with rounded lobes and teeth; sweet edible acorns maturing in one season; loosely scaly bark.

WHITE OAK
(Quercus alba)

Often 30 m or more in height, this tree with its pale grey bark frequently grows in sandy soils and occurs in the Carolinian zone and southern parts of the Mixed Forest region. Leaves have 7-9 narrow, deeply-cut, rounded lobes, are pinkish when unfolding in the spring, and turn dark red in the fall. The 1.3-1.8 cm acorns, which are about a quarter enclosed by the knobby scales, were cooked and eaten by the Indians. Squirrels aid in seed dispersal, since they never recover all the acorns they bury.

BUR OAK
(Quercus macrocarpa)

Growing to about 20 m, Bur Oak has gnarled, corky-ridged branches like Rock Elm. It occurs mainly in bottom lands throughout the Deciduous and Mixed Forest regions of Ontario. The upper half of each leaf is broader and toothed, the lower half has short rounded lobes. White hairs cover the under surface. The 1.8-3 cm acorns are usually two-thirds or more enclosed by a scaly cup which is densely fringed along the upper edge, giving rise to the common names Bur Oak and Mossy-cup Oak.

Chestnut Oak Group — the leaves are regularly toothed rather than lobed, otherwise these trees are similar to White Oaks.

SWAMP WHITE OAK
(Quercus bicolor)

Local in the Carolinian zone and parts of the southern Mixed Forest, this oak grows to 20 m. It occurs in bottom lands and along the edges of swamps. It often looks untidy because the lower drooping branches are not shed. Shiny above and velvety below, the leaves have rounded teeth or uneven shallow lobes and are widest above the middle. Each leaf tapers toward the base. Large acorns, to 3 cm, half to one-third enclosed by the swollen scales, are held on long stalks (2.5-7.5 cm). Several essentially Carolinian species, less common than our other oaks, also belong to this group. The Chinquapin Oaks (*Q. prinoides*) differ from Chestnut Oaks (*Q. prinus*) in having pointed leaf teeth. Chinquapin Oaks (illustrated to the right) also have smaller acorns, and the leaves are usually densely hairy below. Both these oaks occur most often in dry open habitats.

Red or Black Oak Group — lobes and teeth of leaves with sharp points and tipped with bristles; bitter fruits maturing in two seasons, bark ridged and firm.

RED OAK
(Quercus borealis)

Commonly found in the Deciduous and Mixed Forest regions, Red Oak reaches 20-25 m. It often occurs in pure stands on rocky ridges in the Canadian Shield region and in well-drained sandy soils farther to the south, but may grow with other deciduous trees or conifers. The smooth leaves have 7-11 tapering lobes, each forked and bristle-tipped. The V-shaped notches go about halfway to the midrib. The acorns may be either narrow or broad, 1.8 to 3 cm long; the cup, which is shallow and made up of close-fitting scales, usually covers less than one-third of the acorn. The bark is dark brown with broad flat ridges. Red Oak is planted as an ornamental in Europe and grows faster than many other oaks.

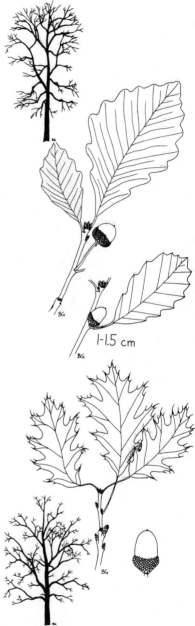

1-1.5 cm

(41)

BLACK OAK
(Quercus velutina)

Primarily a Carolinian species growing to about 20 m high, Black Oak is also found in an area north of eastern Lake Ontario. It occurs most frequently on dry sandy soils. The leaves are shiny dark green above, and rough or scurfy and yellowish green below, whereas both Red and Pin Oak have almost smooth lower leaf surfaces. The 5-7 rectangular leaf lobes are separated by deep U-shaped notches which usually extend nearly to the midrib, while in Red Oak there are less deep V-shaped notches between the tapering lobes. The acorns, 1.3-1.8 cm long, are about half enclosed by the loose-fitting slightly hairy scales. Densely woolly buds are distinctive. The bark is dark brown or nearly black on the surface, but orange inside. This inner bark was used by the early settlers to make a yellow dye. Although many of our oaks are distinctive, the leaves and fruits of some are variable, and hybrids produced between the different species sometimes make identification difficult.

PIN OAK
(Quercus palustris)

Frequently growing 15-20 m tall in a pyramidal or cone shape, Pin Oak is restricted to parts of the Carolinian zone. Many short sturdy branchlets project from the trunk and main branches, like "pins", accounting for its common name. It prefers damp soils along streams, in swamps, and on open prairies. The leaves usually have 5, sometimes 7, widely spreading, narrow, rectangular lobes separated by deep U-shaped notches which extend more than half way to the midrib. They are shiny above, paler below, have teeth tipped with bristles, and are without hairs on the lower surface. Pin Oaks are the earliest oaks to flower. Their nearly round acorns are very small, 1.3 cm or less, and are enclosed in a shallow cup. The mature tree has a distinctive appearance with the lower dead branches widely spreading and drooping. A black ink can be made by adding twigs with insect galls to boiled water which has iron filings in it.

HACKBERRY
(Celtis occidentalis)

Resembling an elm, this small to medium-sized tree, 10-20 m tall, has a rounded crown. Small greenish flowers with 5 petals appear in May. The reddish-purple cherry-like fruits, 8 mm across, are held on long stalks. They are edible and remain on the tree all winter, providing food for many kinds of birds. Coarsely toothed bluish-green leaves, 6-10 cm long, have uneven bases and long tapering tips. The twigs are slender, green or tinged with brown, finely hairy, and have a chambered pith. The greyish-brown bark has dark warty knobs and narrow ridges with corky thickenings. Occurring in the Carolinian zone and parts of the southern Mixed Forest, Hackberry is relatively scarce, growing most often in river-bottom forests. The bark and fruits distinguish Hackberry from the elms. The closely related Dwarf Hackberry (*C. tenuifolia*), a shrub or small tree no more than 8 m high, is known from Point Pelee and Pinery Parks in southwestern Ontario. Its shorter, almost symmetrical, leaves have few or no teeth.

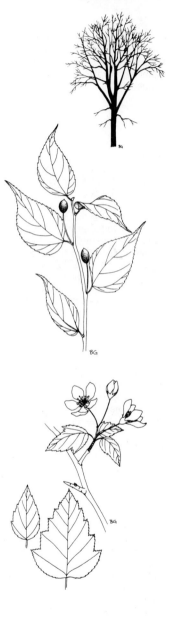

WILD CRAB APPLE
(Pyrus coronaria)

This bushy shrub or small tree, 6-10 m tall, has a short trunk which divides to form a widespreading round-topped crown. It is confined mainly to the Carolinian zone. In May and early June, when the leaves are almost full grown, fragrant rosy-white flowers, 3.5-5 cm across, appear in 5-6 flowered umbels. In late autumn the roundish apple-like fruits, 3.5 cm in diameter, ripen to a yellowish green. The leaves, dark green above and paler beneath, may be lobed but always have irregular, sharp, gland-tipped teeth. Smooth twigs are brownish with bright-red buds. Spine-like spur-shoots develop on older branchlets. Most often found in open woods and along fence rows, this species prefers rich moist soil. The fruits are eaten by many birds. The introduced apple tree (*Malus pumila*), often persisting after cultivation, differs in having downy white hairs covering the under surface of the finely toothed unlobed leaves. The buds and twigs are also hairy.

(43)

ELMS

Elms are among the earliest trees to bloom in spring. Flower clusters open before the leaves unfold, and in only a few weeks the circular winged fruits are mature. The typical elm leaf, supported on a short thick petiole, has uneven leaf bases, is doubly toothed, and has prominent parallel side veins. The dark-grey to reddish-brown bark has flat-topped irregular ridges.

WHITE ELM
(Ulmus americana)

The vase shape is characteristic of White Elm. Trees may reach 35 m, but are usually 18-24 m tall. In April the flowers droop on stalks up to 1.3 cm long. Winged fruits, .5-1 cm, fringed with hairs and notched at the tip, are shed by May. The upper surface of the leaf may be smooth or rough, and the brownish twigs are completely smooth. White Elm occurs from the Carolinian zone north into the southern parts of the Boreal Forest region. Just as the Chestnut blight killed almost all our Sweet Chestnuts, Dutch Elm disease has drastically reduced White Elm, which is the most susceptible of the Ontario elms. In many parts of southern Ontario it was once common, especially along fence rows and in river valleys. Dutch Elm disease, so-called because of the early studies by Dutch scientists, is caused by a fungus that is carried by bark beetles. Probably of Asiatic origin, it was first observed in Europe in 1919 and in North America in 1930, having accidentally been introduced in elm logs imported for veneer. It was first reported in eastern Ontario in 1946, but rapidly spread through most of the province.

SLIPPERY ELM
(Ulmus rubra)

Slippery Elm (to 20 m) is similar in appearance to White Elm except that the trunk is proportionally longer and it has a narrower crown. The flowers are without stalks and are densely clustered. The fruit, with an almost circular papery wing, is about 1-2 cm wide, and only the seed is covered with hairs. Rough grey twigs and dark buds with rusty hairs also separate this species from other elms. Extremely rough on the upper surface, the fragrant leaves are softly hairy beneath. The inner layers of the bark have a slippery consistency, accounting for the common name. Found only in the Carolinian zone and sparingly in the southern Mixed Forest region, Slippery Elm grows in rich soils along streams and on dry rocky ridges.

ROCK ELM
(Ulmus thomasi)

Rock Elm (15-20 m tall) has a relatively long main trunk with numerous horizontally spreading branches. The flowers appear in early spring in elongate clusters with stalks about 1 cm. The fruit, .8-2 cm, is covered with hairs, but the wing is poorly defined and has only a small notch at the tip. The leaves, which are almost even at the base, are very dark green, smooth and shiny above, and slightly hairy beneath. The light reddish-brown twigs soon become thick, developing corky ridges, which account for the name Cork Elm. Rock Elm occurs in the Carolinian zone and also in the southern parts of the Mixed Forest region and is especially prevalent on shallow soils over limestone.

RED MULBERRY
(*Morus rubra*)

This small spreading tree with a short trunk rarely exceeds 10 m. In May and early June, the tiny flowers hang in catkins, opening either before or as the leaves unfold. The fruits (2.5-5 cm) are at first red, becoming dark reddish-purple or black by July. They look like blackberries and are sweet and edible. The yellowish-green leaves, 7-13 cm long, are covered with rough hairs on the under surface. They may be lobed or not, and a great variety of leaf shapes often occurs on a single tree. In autumn the foliage turns yellow. The orangey-brown twigs exude a milky sap when broken and have greenish-brown buds. The reddish-brown older bark ruptures into long flakes. Apparently native to the Carolinian zone, Red Mulberry has been planted as an ornamental or fruit tree elsewhere in southern Ontario, where it has escaped from cultivation. The introduced White Mulberry (*M. alba*), which has also widely escaped, is very similar but has smaller smooth leaves, tasteless whitish to purplish fruits, reddish-brown buds, and yellowish-brown bark.

OSAGE ORANGE
(*Maclura pomifera*)

The remarkable fruits of Osage Orange are unlike those of any other Ontario tree or shrub. They mature in October, are green, wrinkled, and about the size of a grapefruit (9 cm), but are not edible. Reaching 15-20 m, this tree has orangey-brown fibrous bark. The small flowers are produced in tight clusters during May and June, when the leaves are about two-thirds grown. The smooth shiny leaves, 7-13 cm long, which narrow abruptly to slender tips, are without teeth. They turn yellow in the fall and exude a milky sap when broken. The zigzagging twigs bear unbranched thorns just above each leaf. Native to the southeastern United States, Osage Orange was planted as a living fence before barbed wire was available. It has persisted after cultivation and escaped locally to bottom lands in the Carolinian zone. The yellowish wood has a greater density than that of any other Ontario tree, and is so heavy that it barely floats when freshly cut.

6-12 cm

CUCUMBER TREE
(Magnolia acuminata)

The Cucumber Tree, reaching 25 m tall, grows on rich well-drained sites in the Carolinian zone. The solitary bell-shaped flowers open during May and June. They are rather large (to 5 cm long) and resemble Magnolia blossoms, but their greenish-yellow colour renders them less conspicuous. The group of small fleshy pods, on a thick short stem which is 5-7.5 cm long, becomes reddish at maturity. A scarlet seed suspended on a fine white thread is released from each pod. Wavy-edged leaves, about 18 cm long, are broadest near the middle, and abruptly taper to a short sharp tip. White lines encircle the twigs at the top of each horseshoe-shaped leaf scar. The furrowed bark is greyish-brown.

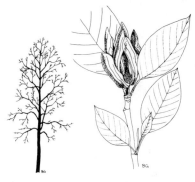

TULIP TREE
(Liriodendron tulipifera)

During May and June, solitary greenish-yellow tulip-like blossoms, from 3-5 cm across, open after the leaves have expanded. The bases of the 6 broad petals are bright orange. The light-brown cone-like fruiting heads, 6 cm long, are made up of many winged nutlets which fall away from the central axis in autumn and winter. The smooth shiny leaves with large stipules and a distinctive broad notch at the top have blades 8-14 cm long. Tulip Trees reach 20-30 m tall. In Ontario they are confined to the Carolinian zone.

BLACK GUM
(Nyssa sylvatica)

Another Carolinian species, often about 15 m high, this tree prefers low wet ground along streams or in swamps. Small clusters of inconspicuous greenish-white flowers occur at the ends of long stalks in May and early June. Male and female flowers grow on separate trees. Ripening in October, the blue berry-like fruits, 8 mm in diameter, occur either singly or 2-3 together. The 5-12 cm leaves are widest above the middle, have wavy-edged margins but no teeth, and turn from a shiny deep green to scarlet in the fall.

(47)

SASSAFRAS
(Sassafras albidum)

Confined to the Carolinian zone, this southern tree, which may be shrubby in the northern parts of its range, reaches 10 m and prefers rich sandy loams. The crown is elongated with a flat top, and branchlets have a staghorn appearance. The leaves, twigs, branches, and bark have a pleasant spicy fragrance. In May, loose clusters of yellowish-green flowers open as the leaves unfold. Shiny, dark-blue, berry-like fruits, 1-1.5 cm long, develop on thick, club-shaped, red stalks. The leaves are 7-15 cm in length, and there may be three kinds on the same tree. Some are unlobed, others mitten-shaped or 3-lobed but all the leaves have 3 major veins toward the base. They turn yellow to red in the fall. The smooth shiny twigs are yellowish-green and brittle with greenish buds. The dark-brownish bark is deeply grooved and has heavy corky ridges. Although the wood is not very important commercially, an orange dye may be produced from the inner bark, and "oil of sassafras" can be distilled from the root, to scent soaps and rubbing lotions. Pioneers prepared a tea from the root bark and drank it as a tonic. Because of its supposed medicinal values, Sassafras was one of the first plant products exported from New England.

SYCAMORE
(Platanus occidentalis)

Occurring rarely in the southern Mixed Forest, Sycamore is a Carolinian zone tree which may grow to 25 m or more, doing best on rich soils along rivers. In May, when the leaves are about a quarter grown, the male and female flowers open in separate heads on the same tree. The brownish "buttonball" fruits, 2.5 cm in diameter, hang on long woody stalks. They are made up of many individual nutlets, each with a circle of hairs at the base. The fruiting heads disintegrate in winter or spring. The leaves, 10-14 cm across, are smooth above but hairy below. They have 3 main veins near the base, and 3-5 lobes with coarsely toothed margins. The base of the leaf stalk is hollow and covers next year's conical bud. Two stipules are conspicuous. The smooth brown bark peels away to the creamy-white inner bark, giving the trunk a striking mottled appearance.

BLACK CHERRY
(Prunus serotina)

Black Cherry trees 15-20 m tall are not uncommon in the Carolinian and southern Mixed Forest regions. They grow best in rich river valleys, but also occur in wet to dry woods. One of the latest cherries to flower, it is not until the first leaves are full grown in May or June that the white 5-petalled flowers, 6 mm across, appear in loose elongated clusters (6-14 cm). Birds are very fond of the almost black fruits (1 cm), which mature by late August or early September. The sepals are retained at the base of the juicy 1-seeded fruit, which is slightly bitter. Fruit pits of cherries should not be eaten, since they contain poisonous cyanic acid. The sharp-pointed leaves, 7-13 cm long, have incurved teeth and short brown hairs along the midrib below. When young, the smooth almost black bark has horizontal streaks (lenticels); later it breaks into squarish scales that curve outward at their edges. The high demand for the valuable wood has resulted in a decline of this species. (See also Choke Cherry, p. 61).

TREE OF HEAVEN
(Ailanthus altissima)

Introduced as an ornamental from China, Tree of Heaven is a very hardy species, which in southern Ontario is beginning to invade our sandy forests and is a city "weed" often growing up through the cracks in cement beside buildings. It grows 10-15 m tall here, but is taller in its native habitat. Greenish-white or yellow flowers, in clusters 20 to 30 cm long, open in June when the leaves have fully developed. Male clusters are larger, contain more flowers, and produce an unpleasant odour. The fruits, 3.5-5 cm long, are yellow or pinkish with a solitary seed in the middle surrounded by a twisted wing. Fruit clusters persist on the tree throughout the winter. The compound alternate leaves, up to 1 m in length, have 13-41 short-stalked nearly opposite (sub-opposite) or alternate leaflets. Leaflets are toothed at the base and have hairs on the under surface. Bruised or broken leaves and twigs smell like old buttered popcorn. Once established, this tree is hard to get rid of, since it grows quickly and has vigorous suckers.

(49)

3-5 cm

MAPLES

The leaves, leaf scars, and buds of maples are arranged opposite one another, and each consecutive pair is rotated 90°. Wind carries the pollen from tree to tree in early spring. Hanging on long stalks, each fruit (sometimes called a "maple key") has 2 seed cases, each with a seed and a wing that acts like a propeller for dispersal by the wind. The bark of young trees is smooth and grey like that of the American Beech.

SUGAR MAPLE
(Acer saccharum)

Canada's national tree, the Sugar Maple, is valued not only for its wood and maple syrup, but also for its beauty. It is often one of the dominants in Carolinian and Mixed forests, doing best in moist, fertile upland soils. It commonly attains a height of 25 m. Saplings, tolerant of shade, can continue to grow at a very slow rate until an opening occurs in the forest. In April and May, yellowish flowers hanging in tassel-like clusters appear with the unfolding leaves. Fruits, 2.5-4 cm long, maturing by fall, have almost parallel wings. The simple leaves, about 10 cm across, have 3-5 palmate lobes with the end lobe almost square. Sugar Maple has distinctive U-shaped notches between the lobes, and the leaf surfaces and leaf stalk are smooth. Fall foliage is yellow, orange, or scarlet. The bark is dark grey with long irregular vertical strips. Because the wood is very hard, Sugar Maple is sometimes called Rock Maple.

BLACK MAPLE
(Acer nigrum)

Very similar to Sugar Maple, the Black Maple differs in having the under surface of its dark-green leaves covered with velvety hairs. Up to 13 cm broad, the leaves are distinctly drooping with their edges curling downward, unlike those of Sugar Maple, which are more or less flat. The fall foliage is yellow or yellowish brown. Black Maple occurs most frequently in rich bottom lands along rivers in the Carolinian zone and portions of the southern Mixed Forest region.

2.5-4.5 cm

(50)

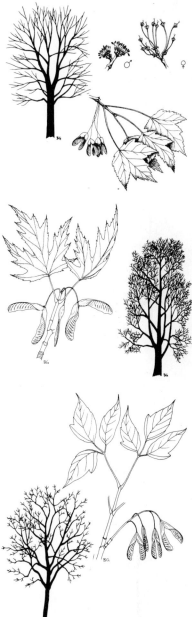

RED MAPLE
(*Acer rubrum*)

Red Maple receives its name from its reddish twigs, buds, flowers, immature fruits, and leaf stalks, as well as scarlet fall foliage. The flowers open before the leaves in March and April. Keys, 1.5-2.5 cm long, mature by midsummer with about a 60° angle between the 2 wings. The smooth leaves are pale below. Shallow notches between the lobes are V-shaped, and the sides of the end lobe are almost parallel. Averaging about 15 m tall, and with softer wood, Red Maple is not as commercially important as Sugar Maple, but is more widespread, occurring north to the Boreal Forest region. Found mainly in swamps, it sometimes grows on drier rocky ground.

SILVER MAPLE
(*Acer saccharinum*)

Silver Maple occurs in swamps or along stream banks of the Carolinian and Mixed Forest regions, often reaching 20-25 m high. This is the first maple to flower, the buds opening in March and early April before the leaves appear. Maturing as early as May, the pale reddish-brown keys are 4-6 cm long with elongate seeds up to 1 cm (often only one develops). Silver Maple leaves are deeply 5-lobed, and the sides of the end lobe diverge in a V. They are silvery-white beneath. This tree is often planted as an ornamental, especially along city streets.

ASH-LEAVED MAPLE
(*Acer negundo*)

Also called Manitoba Maple, this species (10-15 m tall) is our only native maple with compound leaves. Pale-green flowers open with or before the leaves in April and May. In autumn, fruits, 2.5-3.5 cm long, hang in drooping clusters and remain on the tree into the early winter, providing food for Grosbeaks. The seed is long and thin. The smooth yellowish-green leaves (15-40 cm long) with 3-7 leaflets turn yellow in the fall. Frequently found along lake shores and banks of streams, this maple is aggressive and fast growing. It often occurs with Tree of Heaven in vacant city lots.

(51)

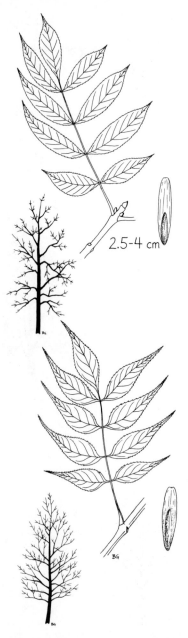

2.5-4 cm

ASHES

Ashes, like maples, have an opposite leaf arrangement, but the leaves are always compound with an odd number of leaflets. These medium-sized trees have ascending branches and trunks that extend to the top of the crown. Flowers appear early in the spring before the leaves emerge. Fruit clusters mature in the autumn and often remain on the tree into winter. Each fruit has a single seed with a long wing that is shaped like a canoe paddle.

BLACK ASH
(Fraxinus nigra)

Black Ash occurs in swamps and bottom lands throughout much of Ontario except in regions beyond the Boreal Forest. It reaches 12-20 m tall. Leaves, 25-40 cm long, have 7-11 finely and sharply toothed leaflets. Each leaflet is green on both sides and has a long slender tip. They are attached without stalks to a rachis which is smooth except for reddish tufts of hairs at the base of the leaflets. The twigs of Black Ash are round and hairy rather than 4-angled and smooth as in Blue Ash. Seed wings, extending all the way from the base of the seed, are blunt at both ends. The light-grey bark is soft with corky ridges, and never has a diamond-shaped pattern. Although not important for lumber, baskets can be woven from the wood.

BLUE ASH
(Fraxinus quadrangulata)

Up to 20 m tall but usually much smaller, Blue Ash is very rare and local in Ontario, occurring only at Point Pelee and in parts of the Thames River valley. The smooth twigs are 4-angled, with corky ridges extending from the sides of the leaf scars. The leaves, 20-30 cm long, are similar to those of Black Ash, except that the 7-11 leaflets are held on short stalks without hairs at the base. Fruits with broad squarish ends are also similar to those of Black Ash. The sap turns blue on exposure to the air, and a blue dye can be made from the inner bark. The whitish bark with scaly plates is unusual for an ash.

WHITE ASH
(Fraxinus americana)

White Ash prefers uplands and well-drained sites, but grows in a variety of situations, often to heights of 20-25 m. It is the most common ash in the Deciduous Forest and occurs throughout the Mixed Forest except in the more northern areas. The leaves, 20-40 cm long, have 5-11 broadly oval leaflets on stalks 0.3-1.5 cm long. This is our only ash that has very pale, almost whitish, leaf under surfaces. Leaflets may or may not be toothed, while their stalks are smooth and not winged. In fall the foliage turns dull purple to yellowish. White Ash differs from Red Ash in having smooth, usually shiny, twigs. The fruits are produced on smooth stalks in dense drooping clusters. They taper at both ends and the wing extends only to the tip of the seed. White Ash differs from Black Ash in having tight diamond-patterned bark, and the buds are rusty and blunt instead of blackish and pointed. The strong tough wood is of high quality for lumber.

3-5 cm

RED ASH
(Fraxinus pennsylvanica)

Growing 10-15 m tall, Red Ash occurs in the Deciduous and Mixed Forest regions, usually in wet areas along stream banks or lake shores. The leaves, which are yellowish-green on both sides, are 18-30 cm long. The 7-9 leaflets have wavy or slightly toothed edges and are joined to the central hairy leaf stalk (rachis) by short winged stalks. These leaflets are covered with downy hairs on the under surface and turn yellowish-brown in autumn. Twigs as well as fruit-bearing stalks are also velvety hairy. Fruits 4-7.5 cm long are borne in open clusters. The slender seeds vary from 1.7 to 3 cm. The wing extends from about the middle of the seed, widening and then gradually tapering to the end. A diamond-shaped pattern develops in the greyish-brown bark, which may be tinged with red. Green Ash, a variety of Red Ash (*subinteger-rima*) is similar in all respects to the typical variety except that it has smaller fruits, 2.7-4.5 cm long, and is almost or completely smooth rather than hairy.

(53)

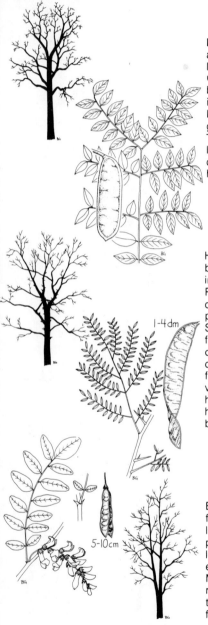

KENTUCKY COFFEE-TREE
(Gymnocladus dioica)

Large doubly compound leaves, 30-90 cm long and up to 60 cm wide, and large pods, 8-25 cm long, make it impossible to mistake the Kentucky Coffee-tree. Reaching 10-15 m tall, it is native to bottom lands in extreme southwestern Ontario, but is planted as an ornamental north to Ottawa. Individual leaflets are about 5 cm long. In June, greenish-white flowers occur in terminal clusters. The greenish pods become reddish-brown and leathery in autumn and remain on the tree throughout the winter. Pioneers are said to have used the hard-shelled beans as a substitute for coffee.

HONEY LOCUST
(Gleditsia triacanthos)

Honey Locust is unique among our native trees because of its robust compound thorns (to 25 cm) in dense clusters on the trunk and main branches. Reaching 20 m high, it grows naturally in Ontario only along the western L. Erie shore but is a popular ornamental elsewhere in southern Ontario. Singly or doubly compound leaves have 18-28 finely toothed leaflets, 1-4 cm long, which are blunt or slightly pointed at the tip and attached to a hairy central stalk (rachis). In June, greenish-white flowers, in drooping clusters 6-8 cm long, are not very showy but produce nectar which attracts honey bees. Thin, twisted, mahogany-red pods have bean-like seeds inside. The smooth dark-brown bark breaks into scaly ridges.

BLACK LOCUST
(Robinia pseudo-acacia)

Black Locust, to 15 m high, has been introduced from the Appalachians and successfully established locally throughout southern Ontario. Compound leaves, 25 cm long, have an odd number of leaflets (7-19), without teeth. White pea-like flowers, 2.5 cm across, are showy and fragrant in late May or early June. Flat reddish-brown "pea-pods" remain on the tree until early winter. Zigzagging twigs have paired spines. Mature bark is deeply furrowed into fibrous ridges.

(54)

Small Trees or Shrubs

NANNYBERRY
(*Viburnum lentago*)

Usually found along shores and the edges of swamps, Nannyberry is our tallest Viburnum. A broad cluster (5-10 cm) of 5-parted flowers develops during late May or early June and produces a sweet scent. By August, the fruits (about 1.3 cm) ripen to bluish-black with a whitish bloom. Opposite leaves are characteristic of all Viburnums, but this species is readily distinguished by its ovate leaf shape, finely toothed margins, and wavy-grooved leaf stalks. Nannyberry is common throughout much of southern Ontario, but is usually found outside the Canadian Shield region.

GREEN ALDER
(*Alnus crispa*)

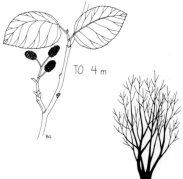

Widespread and frequent over much of northern Ontario, further south Green Alder is rare and confined to cold sites. The younger branches are brownish, hairy, and sticky. The pith of alders is more or less triangular in cross section. In both Speckled and Green Alder the female catkins are cone-like and remain on the plant for a year or more after the seeds are shed, but in Green Alder these "cones" have longer stalks and the seeds have broad wings. In addition, Green Alder differs in having sessile pointed winter buds, and the 4-9 cm leaves are singly toothed.

SPECKLED ALDER
(*Alnus rugosa*)

The male catkins respond early to the coming of spring. In April, when there is still snow and ice about, they elongate and release clouds of yellow pollen. The older stems have a smooth, dark, reddish-brown bark with lighter markings, hence the common name Speckled. Leaves are alternate, 6-10 cm long, smooth above but somewhat hairy below, and, unlike those of Green Alder, they are doubly toothed. Other distinctive features are the stalked blunt winter buds, short-stalked "cones", and narrow winged seeds. Speckled Alder is found along the edges of streams, rivers, and lakes throughout much of Ontario, except the extreme southwest.

WILLOWS (see also p. 34)

A. SHINING WILLOW (*Salix lucida*)
Leaves smooth, shining green above, pale green below. The catkins appear in late May with immature leaves. Mature fruit smooth, less than 7 mm. Bud scales chestnut brown. Widespread in moist places, but especially in southern Mixed Forest region.

B. PEACH-LEAVED WILLOW (*Salix amygdaloides*)
Leaves smooth, pale greyish-green below. Bud scales yellow. Mature fruit smooth, 4-5 mm. Catkins in May with immature leaves. Shores of lakes and streams, mostly in southern Mixed Forest region.

C. AUTUMN WILLOW (*Salix serissima*)
Leaves smooth, shiny, green, and rather thick, with pale-yellow mid-vein, and whitish-green below. Bud scales pale yellow. Mature fruit 7-10 mm, smooth. Catkins appear in June with well-developed leaves. Shores and fens throughout Ontario, rare southward.

D. PUSSY WILLOW (*Salix discolor*)
This and related species are the Pussy Willows used for spring decorations. Catkins appear before the leaves, which are smooth, whitish, and rugose below. Mature fruit 7-10 mm, grey-hairy. Moist swampy places in Mixed and Boreal Forest regions.

E. SLENDER WILLOW (*Salix petiolaris*)
Leaves shiny when young with soft silky hair, but later smooth, pale below. Catkins appear with the leaves. Mature fruit 6-8 mm, thinly hairy. Widespread in Ontario north of Carolinian zone, along shores and in swampy woods.

F. BEAKED WILLOW (*Salix bebbiana*)
One of our most abundant and widespread willows. Leaves are very rugose beneath, and more or less grey-hairy. Mature fruit 7-10 mm, finely hairy.

G. UPLAND WILLOW (*Salix humilis*)
Leaves hairy but not rugose, whitish below. Fruits 7-9 mm, greyish-hairy. Catkins appear before the leaves. Throughout Ontario in open woods and clearings, often in relatively dry sandy or rocky sites.

H. SANDBAR-WILLOW (*Salix interior*)
Leaves smooth and pale below. Catkins appear after leaves. Mature fruit 7-10 mm, smooth. River banks and lake shores. Most abundant in the south.

I. SAGE-LEAVED WILLOW (*Salix candida*)
Leaves greyish above and densely white-hairy below. Mature fruit 6-8 mm, densely white-hairy. Found in fens and along moist alkaline shores, widespread north of Carolinian zone and especially frequent along the shores of Lake Huron.

J. BALSAM WILLOW (*Salix pyrifolia*)
Leaves smooth, whitish below, reddish when young. Crushed foliage has odour of balsam. Mature fruit 6-8 mm, smooth. Bogs, swamps, and shores in Mixed and Boreal Forest regions.

K. HEART-LEAVED WILLOW (*Salix rigida*)
Leaves light silky-hairy when young, becoming smooth. Leaf-like appendages (stipules) at base of leaf stalk 1-2 cm long. Shores of lakes and rivers throughout much of Ontario.

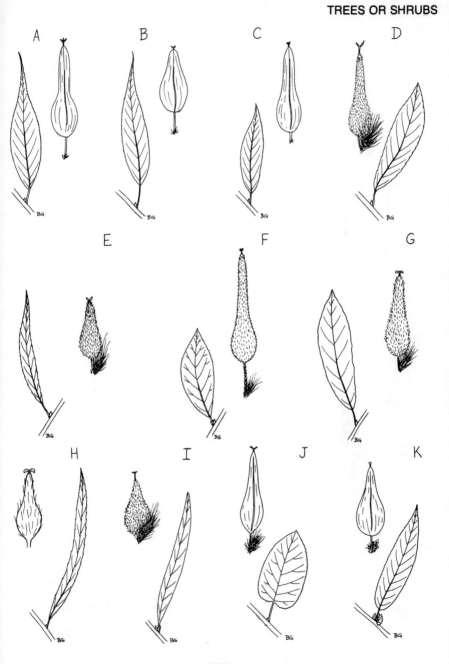

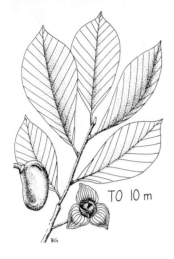

PAWPAW
(Asimina triloba)

The large drooping leaves give this plant a tropical appearance, and indeed many of its close relatives are found in the tropics. Pale greenish-yellow flowers, 3-4 cm across, open in mid- to late May when the leaves have barely emerged; they persist until June and become a dark reddish-purple. The botanical name *triloba* refers to their 3-parted appearance with 3 sepals, 3 large petals, and 3 smaller petals. Greenish fruits, 3-13 cm long, become pale yellow when ripe. They are called "pawpaws" and are sweet and pleasant to eat in the southern parts of their range in the United States but apparently become rather less tasty to the north. In Ontario, Pawpaw is confined to moist woodlands in the Carolinian zone.

STAGHORN SUMAC
(Rhus typhina)

The pinnately compound leaves, with 5-15 pairs of opposite leaflets, and the velvety divergent branches resembling a stag's antlers, make this shrub especially easy to recognize. Tiny greenish flowers are borne in dense terminal clusters 12-25 cm long and appear during late June and early July. The reddish fruit clusters remain after the leaves have fallen, and these, as well as the twigs, are an important food source for wildlife ranging from moose to rabbits, grouse, and pheasants. This shrub is a primary colonizer of old fields and clearings, brightening the woodland edges with scarlet, orange, and yellow in the autumn. It is common in southern Ontario, but extends locally into northern Ontario.

The Smooth Sumac (*R. glabra*), .5-3 m in height, is similar, but has smooth twigs and is less common.

The Poison Sumac (*R. vernix*), which produces in some people a severe skin irritation like Poison Ivy, also has pinnately compound leaves, but the margins of the leaflets are smooth and the white berries are borne on drooping clusters. Reaching 5 m, Poison Sumac is found in swampy places in the Carolinian zone, though it is rare farther north.

(58)

WITCH-HAZEL
(Hamamelis virginiana)

The foliage turns a bright yellow in the autumn and, as the leaves fall in late September and October, the curious flowers appear, each with 4 twisted yellow petals. The capsule does not mature until the following autumn, so that the seeds are shed while the shrub is in flower. These peculiarities are only the beginning. The capsule is an "exploding" fruit, contracting and building up pressure until it splits open very suddenly with violent force, discharging the two black seeds like miniature bullets, sometimes to distances of 12 m. The empty capsules are persistent for another season after liberating the seeds, and help to identify this shrub during the winter. An oil distilled from the twigs of Witch-hazel (and marketed under the same name) has a great many medicinal uses, including treatment of such regular ailments as insect bites, bruises, and burns. The astringent qualities of this oil has resulted in its use in cosmetics, and it is reputed to be of particular use in eliminating "bags" under the eyes. Witch-hazel is found in dry sandy soil in open oak woodlands and on drier slopes, from the Carolinian zone sparingly northward to the Ottawa district.

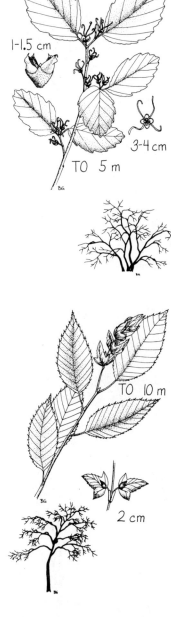

BLUE BEECH
(Carpinus caroliniana)

The firm bluish-green leaves have a smooth texture. They differ from those of true Beech in having smaller teeth between the larger teeth at the end of each vein, and in turning red rather than yellow in the autumn. In winter the Blue Beech has much shorter buds, 2-4 mm. The bark is smooth, slate-grey in colour, and the trunk has longitudinal muscle-like ridges that give it the common name Muscle Beech. Male and female flower clusters appear on the same plant in early spring. The small ribbed nuts are attached to leaf-like bracts, which probably aid in wind dispersal. The wood is extremely hard, like that of Hop-hornbeam, and was used by the early settlers to make wedges for splitting other logs. Found in the Carolinian and southern Mixed Forest regions. Blue Beech is shade tolerant, forming part of the understory in moist rich woods.

(59)

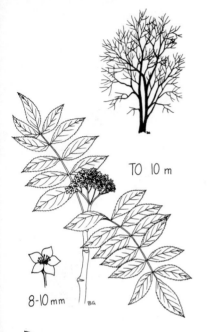

TO 10 m

8-10 mm

AMERICAN MOUNTAIN-ASH
(Sorbus americana)

Distinguishing features include long leaflets that taper gradually to a point and are usually 3-5 times as long as they are wide, fruit 4-6 mm thick, and petals that are longer than the stamens. The white flower clusters appear in May and June, and the orangey-red fruit matures in August. The fruit of this and other Mountain-Ashes looks like a berry, but in fact, from a botanical viewpoint, it is similar to an apple in that the flesh is largely derived from a saucer-shaped floral axis. The 5-parted flowers and numerous stamens also suggest a relationship to apples and to other members of the Rose family. In both this and the following species, the bark is greyish-green with widely spaced horizontal pores, becoming somewhat scaly with age. In the open a short trunk with spreading branches is characteristic, but in the shaded forest an elongate trunk develops. Found on rocky slopes, swamp edges, in clearings and open woods, this Mountain-ash occurs throughout Ontario, except in the far north, but it is rare south of the Canadian Shield region.

TO 10 m

6-8 mm

SHOWY MOUNTAIN-ASH
(Sorbus decora)

This is an especially attractive shrub, with showy white flower clusters in June, large scarlet "berries" in August, and its low bushy form when grown in the open. It differs from the species above in that the leaflets taper more abruptly at the tip and are 2-3 times as long as they are wide. The fruit is 8-12 mm thick, and the petals are approximately the same length as the stamens. It may be found in habitats similar to those of the American Mountain-ash, and has a similar distribution, being absent from the extreme north and very rare in the extreme south. The European Mountain-ash (*S. aucuparia*), which has hairy leaflets rounded at the tip and densely white-woolly buds, is commonly cultivated and frequently escapes to natural habitats, especially in the south. Berries of both native and introduced species are favourite winter foods of birds such as Waxwings, and the increasing popularity of these shrubs as garden ornamentals probably accounts for the increasing abundance of Waxwings in urban areas during winter.

(60)

PIN CHERRY
(Prunus pensylvanica)

Found along woodland edges and in clearings, Pin Cherry occurs throughout most of Ontario. Leaf teeth are small and rounded. Less than 12 white flowers, each about 12 mm across, are borne in umbel-like clusters in May and early June. Bright-red cherries, 6 mm in length and with a sour but edible flesh, ripen in August and September. Black Cherry (p. 49) differs in having leaves with dense hairs on the mid-vein below, and flowers and fruits in a raceme. The wild Plums have larger pale-red or yellowish fruits 2-3 cm, with a flattened and two-edged, rather than a globular stone. Canada Plum (*P. nigra*) has flowers in clusters of 3 or 4, and mature leaves with rounded but much larger leaf teeth 1-3 mm in length.

CHOKE CHERRY
(Prunus virginiana)

More than 20 flowers in an elongate cluster (raceme), and leaves with numerous, narrow, spreading teeth, are distinctive features of Choke Cherry. The white flowers, about 1 cm across, appear in late May and June, terminating new leafy branches of the season. Dark red or black cherries, 8-10 mm in diameter, ripen in August and September. Choke Cherry is found throughout much of Ontario in open woods and at woodland edges. The Black Cherry (p. 49) differs in having incurved and apparently rounded leaf teeth, and the calyx persists where the stalk joins the maturing fruit. In Choke Cherry the calyx disappears as the flowers wither.

SAND CHERRY
(Prunus pumila)

A few to several white flowers, up to 1.5 cm across, appear in umbel-like clusters from mid-May to early June. The leaves are smooth-edged at the base and toothed toward the tip, the teeth being 1-4 mm apart. Sand Cherry is found on shoreline sand dunes about the Great Lakes. On acid granite ridge-tops and sandplains, a wider-leaved species (*P. susquehanae*) is found, its leaves less than three times as long as they are wide.

TO 10 m

TO 10 m

1 m

(61)

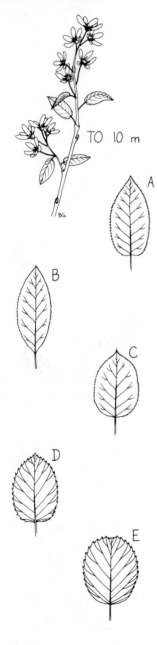

TO 10 m

JUNEBERRIES

Shadbush, Serviceberry

Juneberries usually have flowers in elongate clusters (racemes), and floral parts are attached to top of ovary. Flowers in May and June, often before leaves fully expanded. Berry-like fruits, 5-8 mm, ripen in July and August, and the remains of the floral parts usually persist at the end opposite the stalk.

A. *Amelanchier arborea* (to 10 m)
More than 6 flowers in racemes. Top of ovary smooth. Leaves taper abruptly to a long point; and have more than 25 fine teeth on each side. Open woods and woodland edges in Carolinian and Mixed Forest regions.

B. *Amelanchier bartramiana* (to 3 m)
Differs from other Juneberries in having flowers and fruits in clusters of less than 4 (often only 1 or 2 together), instead of many-flowered (fruited) racemes. Leaves elliptical with numerous fine teeth. Bogs, open rocky clearings; mostly in northern Ontario, rare south of Canadian Shield.

C. *Amelanchier spicata* (to 3 m)
Leaves finely toothed, teeth always less than 1 mm. Top of ovary hairy. Flowering racemes more than 2.5 cm long with more than 6 flowers. Shorelines, river banks, open woods. Widespread.

D. *Amelanchier sanguinea* (to 4 m)
Leaves rather coarsely veined and toothed; the teeth over 0.7 mm during flowering, becoming more than 1 mm long when leaves fully expanded. Top of ovary hairy. Flowers usually 7-9 in raceme more than 3 cm long, becoming more than 4 cm in fruit. Widespread in Ontario; open woods and woodland edges.

E. *Amelanchier alnifolia* (to 1.3 m)
Similar to preceding in its coarsely toothed and coarsely veined leaves, but flowering racemes more compact and dense, being less than 2.5 cm long, and less than 4 cm long in fruit. Throughout Ontario but most common on limestone plateaus in the south. Western variety known as the Saskatoon.

THE HAWTHORNS

The Hawthorns (*Crateagus* spp.) belong to the Rose family and share with other members of this family (Juneberries, Cherries, etc.) floral features such as a 5-parted calyx, 5 horizontally spreading petals, numerous stamens, and various non-floral characters such as alternate leaves with stipules. Cherries differ in having floral parts attached below the ovary. The Juneberries are similar in having the floral parts attached at the top of the ovary (and later the fruit), but they are without thorns and their flowers and fruits are usually in elongated racemes rather than in branched clusters. Hawthorns flower in spring and early summer. The berry-like fruits, like tiny apples 1-1.5 cm thick, may be greenish, red, or yellow. The fruits and the leaves associated with flowering or fruiting branches (floral leaves) are important in identification. Hawthorns are found in pastures, woodland edges, second growth forests, and similar disturbed sites.

A. **ROUND-LEAVED HAWTHORN** (to 7 m)
   (*Crateagus rotundifolia*)
Floral leaves narrowing to the basal stalk and clearly lobed.

B. **COCKSPUR-THORN** (to 10 m)
   (*Crataegus crus-galli*)
Floral leaves narrowed at the base, and unlobed, glossy above, thick. Mature fruit hard and dry with 1 or 2 nutlets.

C. **DOTTED HAWTHORN** (to 10 m)
   (*Crateagus punctata*)
Floral leaves similar to the preceding but dull. Mature fruit becoming succulent, usually with 3-5 nutlets.

D. **SOFT HAWTHORN** (to 12 m)
   (*Crataegus mollis*)
Floral leaves broad at the base, often lobed. Leaves, fruit, and flower stalks hairy.

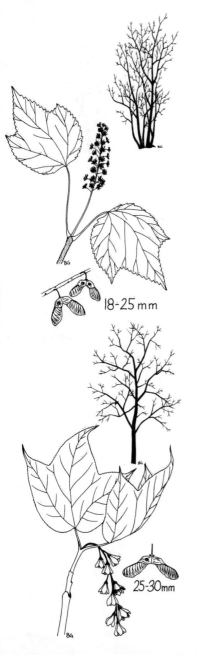

18-25 mm

25-30mm

MOUNTAIN MAPLE
(Acer spicatum)

The branches of our smallest eastern Maple usually ascend from several trunks joined at or near the ground level. Greenish-yellow flowers, less than 1 cm across, appear in dense elongate upright clusters in June, after the leaves are fully grown. The fruit matures in autumn on a drooping raceme, and like other Maples is comprised of two adjoining seeds, each with a wing. The foliage turns red, yellow, or brown in the autumn. The striking brilliant red fruits and autumn foliage of some forms have led to its use in ornamental plantings. Mature bark is reddish-brown, smooth or slightly furrowed, but without the conspicuous white streaks so characteristic of Striped Maple. This species also differs from Striped Maple in having fine greyish hairs on the twigs, erect flower clusters, smaller flowers, smaller buds (less than 6 mm), and a greater number of smaller leaf teeth. Mountain Maple is an understory shrub, especially in rocky and hilly woodlands, extending from the Carolinian zone to the southern Boreal Forest region.

STRIPED MAPLE
(Acer pensylvanicum)

This shrub is sometimes called Moosewood. The twigs and buds are a favourite browse of porcupine, deer, and moose. Yellowish-green flowers, 1.5-2 cm across, appear in drooping clusters in May and June. The twigs are smooth, red or greenish, and the foliage turns a distinctive bright yellow in the autumn. The bark is green or reddish-brown with longitudinal white streaks, which become dull greyish with age. A single trunk is characteristic and is sometimes over 25 cm in diameter. Striped Maple produces the largest leaves of any eastern Maple, sometimes up to 25 cm wide, but more often 10-20 cm. These large leaves droop on arching branches, rather like those of Black Maple (p. 50). Found in shaded situations in cool moist woods, it is confined in Ontario to the southern Mixed Forest region.

EASTERN FLOWERING DOGWOOD
(Cornus florida)

Whether considered a tree or a shrub, Flowering Dogwood is certainly very attractive. Although the flower clusters, which appear in late May, are small and pale greenish, they are surrounded by 4 large pink-and-white bracts resembling petals, each bract having a reddish notch at the end. These notched bracts create the impression of a single very showy flower that is 6 cm across. This "flower" of our largest Dogwood is similar to that of the Bunchberry, our smallest member of the genus *Cornus.* Shiny, red, berry-like fruits ripen during August and September and are about 1.3 cm long. Older bark is reddish-brown and broken into small scales. In autumn the foliage turns various shades from scarlet to deep reddish-brown. The striking flower clusters and attractive autumn foliage make Flowering Dogwood a popular ornamental in the southern parts of the province where it can be grown. Usually found in acid sandy soils in open woods, its natural distribution does not extend outside the Carolinian zone.

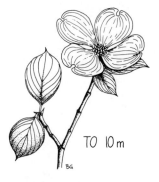

TO 10 m

ALTERNATE-LEAVED DOGWOOD
(Cornus alternifolia)

The whitish or creamy flowers are borne in flat-topped clusters and, like other Dogwoods, they differ from Viburnums in that the floral parts are in fours rather than fives. Flowers appear in May and June, and the dark-blue, berry-like fruits, less than 1 cm long, ripen on red stalks during July and August. The smooth leaves are dark green above and greyish-green below, and unlike our other Dogwoods, they occur in groups and are alternate on the twigs. The branches are also alternate and usually arranged in distinct horizontal layers, perhaps giving rise to the common name Pagoda Tree. The bark is reddish-brown and smooth, becoming broken into shallow ridges with age. Found in the Deciduous and Mixed Forest regions, Alternate-leaved Dogwood is a shade-tolerant understory species in rich woodlands.

TO 6 m

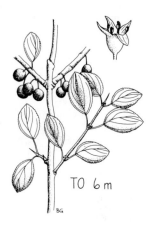

COMMON BUCKTHORN
(Rhamnus cathartica)

The smooth leaves 3-6 cm long may be opposite or alternate and usually have a distinctive fold at the tip. The veins curve toward the tip, like those of Dogwood. The foliage remains green late into the autumn, a characteristic shared with other plants introduced from Europe. Small greenish-yellow flowers appear in dense clusters in the leaf axils in early June. Purplish-black berry-like fruits, 5-6 mm long, ripen in August and September and normally have 2 or 4 stones. Spines occur where twigs divide and at the tips of some branches. The botanical name *cathartica* alludes to the fact that the fruits were once used medicinally as a cathartic, or laxative, but the results were so violent that their use was discontinued early in the history of botanical medicine. The fruits of all Buckthorns should be treated as poisonous. Common Buckthorn is found in woodlands and clearings in southern Ontario, often growing alongside our native trees and shrubs as if it has always been a part of the natural setting.

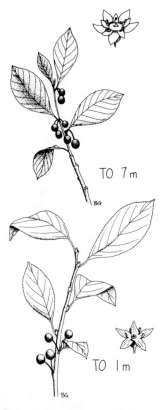

GLOSSY BUCKTHORN
(Rhamnus frangula)

The smooth shiny leaves, 4-8 cm long, and purplish-black berry-like fruits with 3 or rarely 2 stones are good field marks. In June, 1 to several small greenish-yellow flowers protrude from the leaf axils. The fruits are red at first, becoming purplish-black when ripe. This introduced European shrub has become locally abundant in moist woods about cities and towns in southern Ontario.

ALDER-LEAVED BUCKTHORN
(Rhamnus alnifolia)

The alternate leaves, reaching 10 cm in length, are green above and greyish-green below. Small, 5-parted, yellowish-green flowers appear on short stalks below the leaves in late May and June. The purplish-black, berry-like fruits, 6-8 mm long, usually have 3 stones and ripen in August and September. The Alder-leaved Buckthorn is found throughout Ontario in open fens and calcium-rich wetlands, where it forms low thickets.

Shrubs

SWEET-FERN
(Myrica asplenifolia)

The long, slender, pinnately lobed leaves (6-12 cm) suggest fern foliage, but Sweet-fern differs from true ferns in having woody stems and in producing flowers and seeds rather than spores. Flowering occurs in spring, with the male flowers borne in catkins (1.5-2.5 cm) and the female flowers in dense bristly clusters. The groups of ripened nuts are surrounded by bristly scales forming a bur-like mass about 2 cm across. The shrub has a pleasant spicy fragrance. Sweet-fern flourishes in dry acid soils in rocky or sandy regions. It develops sucker growth from long creeping roots, thereby surviving the fires which are sometimes common in the dry areas where it is found. Fire is probably as important in maintaining the Oak scrub and Jack Pine barrens where Sweet-fern occurs as it is in maintaining prairie vegetation. The Ontario distribution of Sweet-fern includes the Boreal and Mixed Forest regions. In southern Ontario it is rather uncommon away from the Canadian Shield.

TO 1 m

SWEET GALE
(Myrica gale)

Sweet Gale is closely related to Sweet-fern, and is also fragrant, but is found in a very different habitat. It occurs in damp soil of bogs, fens, swamps and lake margins where it often grows alongside Leather-leaf (p. 86). It can be distinguished from the latter at a distance by its lighter foliage, and on closer inspection by its obovate leaves (3-6 cm), which have several teeth near the tip and scattered resin dots on the under surface (under 10X magnifier). The inconspicuous flowers are borne in short cone-like catkins. Leaves, twigs, and fruits of Sweet Gale were once collected and hung in cloth bags in clothes closets and drawers, where they kept out the clothes moths and gave a pleasant odour to the clothing. The distribution of Sweet Gale in Ontario extends from the Mixed Forest region north to James Bay. It is fairly common in the "cottage country" of the southern Canadian Shield.

TO 1.5 m

HAZELNUTS

Hazelnuts differ from Birch and Alder in having non-winged fruits and the female flowers in clusters instead of in catkins or "cones". Their shrub-like form with many stems arising from the ground help to distinguish Hazelnuts from young Birches. The male flowers are borne in catkins that are well-formed by August, but remain short and hard throughout the fall and winter. The clusters of female flowers produce tufts of crimson stigmas. Flowering occurs in April, and in some parts of their range Hazelnuts are among the earliest spring flowers. The hazelnuts or filberts that we enjoy especially at Christmas come from a European species of Hazel and are imported from Europe or the west coast of the United States, where they are grown commercially. The North American hazelnuts are similar or even superior in taste to the imported hazelnuts, but are smaller in size. The nuts as well as the twigs are food for a wide range of mammals and birds, and the shrubs also provide good cover for wildlife.

BEAKED HAZELNUT
(Corylus cornuta)

Twigs and leaf stalks are smooth or may have scattered long hairs. The nut (to about 1.5 cm) ripens in August and September. It is enclosed in united bracts that are densely bristly at the base and form a long tubular beak. The elongated catkins are usually less than 4 cm in length. Found in open woods and along woodland edges, Beaked Hazelnut extends from the Carolinian zone north to the Boreal Forest region.

AMERICAN HAZELNUT
(Corylus americana)

The twigs and leaf stalks have a dense covering of glandular hairs. The nuts (to about 1.5 cm), which ripen in August and September, are enclosed in two separate fringed bracts that are often sticky. Catkins become 4-8 cm in length at flowering time. American Hazelnut occurs in clearings and open woods in the Carolinian zone and sparingly northward to Lake Simcoe and the St. Lawrence River.

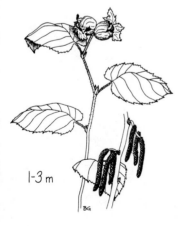

1-3 m

1-3 m

(68)

SWAMP BIRCHES
(Betula pumila var. glandulifera)

The leaves are leathery, dark-green above, 2-3.5 cm long, and coarsely toothed with 3-6 veins on each side. The flowers and fruits are borne in catkins up to 2 cm long. Swamp Birches are found in fens and other open calcium-rich wetlands. Their distribution in Ontario includes much of the north, but in southern Ontario they are virtually absent from the Canadian Shield and from most of the Carolinian zone.

PRICKLY ASH
(Zanthoxylum americanum)

A plant of Prickly Ash is either male or female. The small greenish flowers open in May before the leaves are out. Reddish-brown fruits, ripening in July and August, contain 1 or 2 shiny black seeds. The compound leaves (to 25 cm) have small inconspicuous prickles but large persistent thorns develop at the leaf base. A dense thicket of Prickly Ash is a more effective barrier than a barbed-wire fence! The foliage and fruits are pleasantly aromatic. Prickly Ash occurs in southern Ontario north to the Ottawa district. It is a northern member of the Rue family, to which the citrus fruits belong.

SPICEBUSH
(Lindera benzoin)

Spicebush begins and ends the season with a flourish of yellow. The small yellow flowers appear in dense clusters in late April and May before the leaves are out, and the leaves (4 to 15 cm) turn yellow in the autumn. Small berries (1 cm) ripening in August and September are shiny red and contain a single seed. Like Sassafras (p. 48), Spicebush belongs to the Laurel family and the crushed foliage and twigs of both are aromatic. It is said to have been used to reduce fever, and as a substitute for Allspice during the American War of Independence. Such uses have led to common names such as Fever Bush and Wild Allspice. Spicebush occurs in moist woods in the Carolinian zone and locally northward to the base of the Bruce Peninsula.

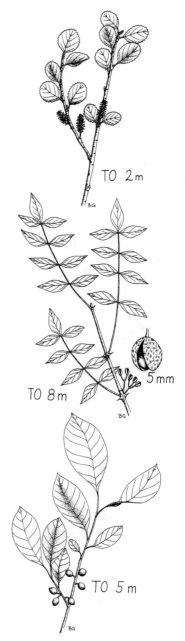

TO 2m

TO 8m

5mm

TO 5m

CURRANTS AND GOOSEBERRIES
(Ribes spp.)

Wild currants and gooseberries have potential value in plant breeding because of their edible berries, but some are also significant as alternate hosts of the White Pine Blister Rust. Flowers have 5 stamens, 5 sepals, and 5 petals, and the fruit is a many-seeded berry. Currants have flowers and fruits in elongate racemes and most are without spines or prickles, while the gooseberries have branched clusters of 2-4 flowers and the stems are usually armed. Maple and Viburnum saplings differ in having opposite leaves. Currants and gooseberries occur in a variety of habitats, including open rocky woods, woodland edges, swamps, slopes, and shorelines.

WILD RED CURRANT
(Ribes triste)

The greenish-purple saucer-shaped flowers, about 6 mm across, are borne in drooping racemes in May and early June. The smooth berries, up to 1 cm in diameter, are bright red and ripen in July and August. Stems are reclining and without spines or prickles. Unlike the Black Currant, the leaves are without resin dots. Wild Red Currant occurs throughout most of Ontario. The cultivated Red Currant (*R. sativum*) has upright stems, yellowish or greenish flowers, flower stalks with gland-tipped hairs, and larger juicy red berries. In southern Ontario it has escaped from cultivation to open woods, steep river banks, and woodland edges.

SKUNK CURRANT
(Ribes glandulosum)

This species is similar to the preceding, but the ovary and red berries have gland-tipped bristles. The berries are not only distasteful but have a skunk-like odour when bruised! Absent from the Carolinian zone and characteristic of cold sites elsewhere in southern Ontario, Skunk Currant is widespread northward. The Bristly Black Currant (*R. lacustre*) also has a raceme of bristly fruits, but differs in having densely spiny stems. Although widespread in northern Ontario, it becomes rare southward and is not found in the Carolinian zone.

3-3.5 mm

TO 2 m

0.5 cm

WILD BLACK CURRANT
(Ribes americanum)

The creamy to yellowish bell-shaped flowers about 1 cm long are borne in drooping racemes and appear in May and early June. Black edible berries, up to 1 cm in diameter, ripen in July and August and have a smooth surface. The erect stems are without spines and prickles, and the leaves have shiny resin dots that are especially conspicuous on the lower surface. Wild Black Currant is widespread in southern Ontario outside the Canadian Shield and occurs in parts of northern Ontario. The cultivated Black Currant (*R. nigrum*), which sometimes escapes to natural habitats, is similar, but has greenish-white to purplish flowers, with bracts shorter than the flower or fruit stalk. The Hudson Bay Currant (*R. hudsonianum*) has upright flower and fruit clusters.

PRICKLY GOOSEBERRY
(Ribes cynosbati)

The greenish-yellow bell-shaped flowers up to 1 cm long are borne in clusters of 2 or 3 and appear in May and early June. The ovary and, later, the reddish-purple berry which ripens in July and August are covered with stiff sharp spines. The stems have spines at the nodes where the branches and leaves are attached, but are smooth elsewhere except in an unusual variety (*atrox*) in which they are densely prickly. Prickly Gooseberry is common in southern Ontario, becoming rare northward.

WILD GOOSEBERRY
(Ribes hirtellum)

Flowers appear in May and June in clusters of 2-4. They are narrowly bell-shaped and greenish or purplish. Blue-black berries, to 1.2 cm, are smooth and edible, ripening in July and August. Younger stems have spines at the nodes and sometimes scattered prickles. These are soon shed with the outer bark. Wild Gooseberry occurs throughout much of Ontario, but in the north it becomes difficult to separate from the closely related Bristly Wild Gooseberry (*R. oxycanthoides*), from which it differs in having longer stamens equal to the sepals and floral bracts with a fringe of long hairs instead of shorter gland-tipped hairs.

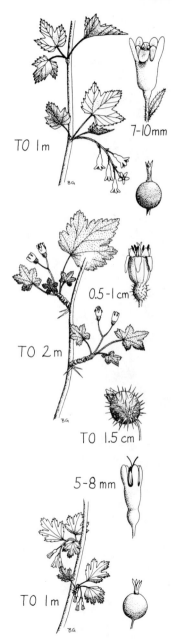

TO 1m

7-10mm

0.5-1 cm

TO 2m

TO 1.5 cm

5-8 mm

TO 1m

(71)

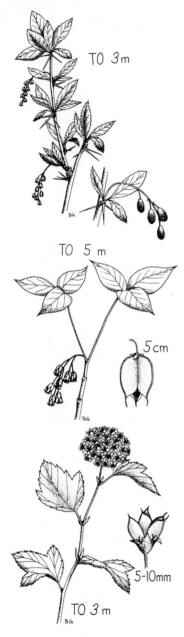

COMMON BARBERRY
(Berberis vulgaris)

Small yellow 6-parted flowers, 8 mm across, are borne in drooping clusters in May and June. Pollinating insects touch the base of the filament while collecting nectar, causing the stamen to spring forward and deposit pollen on the insect's head. Pollen so placed encounters the stigma of the next flower visited. The oblong berries (about 1 cm) are bright scarlet. Alternate leaves (1-6 cm) are spiny-toothed, and the stems have spines in clusters of 3 at the nodes. Common Barberry was once cultivated and has escaped to fields and clearings in southern Ontario. Its popularity has declined since it was found to be the alternate host of a rust fungus that infects wheat crops. The Japanese Barberry (*B. thunbergii*), also an escape from cultivation, differs in having smooth-edged leaves.

BLADDERNUT
(Staphylea trifolia)

White or creamy flowers about 1 cm long appear in drooping clusters in May. The remarkable and distinctive fruit matures by September. It is an inflated papery brown capsule 5-8 cm long with 3 points, each with a bristle-tip. Leaflets are up to 10 cm long. Bladdernut is found in open woods and along stream banks. In Ontario it is mostly confined to the Carolinian zone, though it extends sporadically northward to the Ottawa district.

Hop Tree (*Ptelea trifoliata*), which also has trifoliate leaves, but winged fruits much like those of Elm, is rare and local in the Carolinian zone.

NINEBARK
(Physocarpus opulifolius)

The shreddy bark and palmate leaves are characteristics shared with currants and gooseberries, but the persisting fruits (5-10 mm) of Ninebark are distinctive. The white flowers (7-10 mm) appear in June and July. Flower clusters are often abundant, and because of their numerous protruding stamens they have the soft appearance of *Spiraea* spp. Ninebark occurs in moist rocky or gravelly places throughout much of Ontario.

NARROW-LEAVED MEADOWSWEET
(Spiraea alba)

Our most common species of *Spiraea* is found throughout much of Ontario, usually in marshes and along shores, but also in wet meadows and sometimes in apparently dry sites in the north. The younger stems are orange or yellowish brown. The leaves are smooth and mostly 3-4 times as long as wide. The white or light-pinkish flowers, 6-8 mm in diameter, are borne on long finely hairy inflorescence branches from late June to early August. Like other *Spiraea* spp., they have 5 petals, 5 sepals, and 15 or more erect stamens that give the flower cluster a "fuzzy" appearance.

BROAD-LEAVED MEADOWSWEET
(Spiraea latifolia)

This is similar to the Narrow-leaved Meadowsweet but has wider leaves, 2-3 times as long as wide, and smooth inflorescence branches. Like the Narrow-leaved Meadowsweet it is found throughout much of Ontario, but is apparently less common, especially in the south. Flowering occurs from early July to September, depending upon location. In many members of the Rose family, the seeds are enclosed in a juicy or fleshy fruit, but in our *Spiraea* spp., each flower gives rise to a cluster of 5-8 non-fleshy fruits each 1.5-3 mm. These persist on the shrub over winter, and even into the flowering period of the next season.

STEEPLEBUSH
(Spiraea tomentosa)

Steeplebush, with its long spire-like inflorescence, differs from the above species in having leaves that are densely hairy and light-coloured below. The flowers are usually deep pink or pinkish-purple, and, like other *Spiraea* spp., the flowers at the top of the stalk open first. Flowering occurs from late July to early September. The persisting dry fruits, usually less than 2 mm, are smaller than those of Meadowsweets and have dense cobwebby hairs around the base, giving the inflorescence a frosted appearance. Steeplebush is quite frequent in marshes, bogs, and clearings, and along shores in the Mixed Forest region, but is rare south of the Canadian Shield.

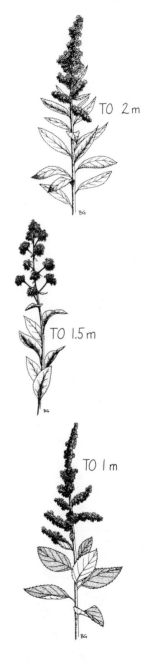

TO 2 m

TO 1.5 m

TO 1 m

(73)

ROSES
(Rosa spp.)

The Rose fruit, usually called a "hip", is composed of a cup-shaped receptacle which becomes fleshy and bright orange or red, with numerous "seeds" inside. Hips have a high vitamin C content, and may be used in the preparation of excellent teas. The Swamp Rose (*R. palustris*), found in swamps of the Carolinian and Mixed Forest region has finely toothed leaves and stout recurved spines. Pasture Rose (*R. carolina*), with coarsely-toothed leaves (teeth 1 mm) and slender spines, occurs in dry open situations in southern Ontario. These two are less common than those illustrated and described below, and differ in two ways: the lower parts of the flower and flower stalk have glandular hairs instead of being smooth; the sepals are often shed instead of being erect and persistent on the mature hip. The introduced Sweetbrier (*R. eglanteria*) occasionally escapes from cultivation. It differs from other species in having resinous glands on the under surface of the leaf. Also introduced, Scotch Rose (*R. multiflora*) is valued by conservationists as food and cover for wildlife. It has distinctive deeply cut stipules.

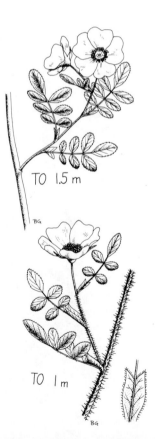

SMOOTH WILD ROSE
(Rosa blanda)

Found in dry more or less open habitats, this species is common throughout southern Ontario northward to the Boreal Forest region. The floral bracts, stipules, and leaf rachis are often not conspicuously glandular, and the plants are unarmed, or with prickles on only the oldest, lowermost branches. Pink flowers, about 7 cm across, appear in late May and June.

PRICKLY WILD ROSE
(Rose acicularis)

Prickly Wild Rose is common throughout much of northern Ontario, occurring in old fields and open woods, and on steep banks, but appears to be much less common in southern Ontario. It is often glandular, and the stems (including the upper ones) are armed with numerous prickles. Pink flowers, 5-7 cm across, appear in June and early July.

BLACK CHOKEBERRY
(Aronia melanocarpa)

Black Chokeberry differs from Purple Chokeberry in that the younger twigs, flower stalks, and lower leaf surfaces are smooth instead of hairy. White 5-parted flowers, 8-12 mm in diameter, appear in late May and June. The fruits ripen to black by August and are 6-8 mm across. Deciduous alternate leaves, 2-8 cm long, are rather thick; they are dark green above and paler beneath. Black Chokeberry may be found in swamps, in bogs, and on rocky (granite) slopes and hilltops. It occurs in the Carolinian and Mixed Forest regions of Ontario.

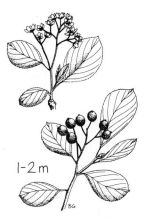

1-2 m

PURPLE CHOKEBERRY
(Aronia prunifolia)

The Purple Chokeberry is hairy on the younger twigs, the flower stalks, and the under surface of the leaves. It has relatively large purplish fruits, 8-10 mm across. White 5-parted flowers, 8-12 mm in diameter, appear in June, and the fruit is usually ripe by August. Except for the velvety texture, the foliage is similar to that of the preceding species and becomes bright red in the autumn. Reddish "hairs" along the mid-vein on the upper side of the leaves of Chokeberries help to distinguish them from the Cherries and Juneberries with which they often occur. Purple Chokeberry is found in swamps, bogs, and rocky open woods, and on hilltops. Like Black Chokeberry, it occurs in the Carolinian and Mixed Forest regions. Most Ontario Chokeberries seem to fit the description of either the Purple or Black Chokeberry (or something in between). The status of the Red Chokeberry (*A. arbutifolia*) in Ontario is still not clear. It is quite similar to the Purple Chokeberry, but has smaller red fruits 4-7 mm across. Only the ripened fruits (maturing in August and September) should be considered in identification. Red Chokeberry is often mistaken for one of the other Chokeberries, because its immature fruits differ in both size and colour from those that have fully ripened.

TO 3 m

BRAMBLES

Raspberries, Blackberries, Dewberries, and Cloudberry differ from other members of the Rose family in having flowers with a large number of separate ovaries that develop into a mass of small fleshy fruits (an "aggregation of drupelets"). Some Brambles are herbaceous from creeping woody stems, but are treated here because of their similar fruits. The shrubs produce stems from the perennial base, which last for two years. During the first year they are without flowers and are called primocanes. During the second year lateral flowering shoots develop on the stems, which are then called floricanes. The leaves of primocanes and floricanes often differ. Brambles are of particular value to wildlife, providing both food and cover.

RED RASPBERRY
(Rubus strigosus)

The stems have slender-based spines and stiff bristles, and the compound leaves are pale below with soft greyish hair. White or greenish-white flowers up to 15 mm across are borne in umbel-like clusters of 2-5. The edible red "berries", 1 cm in diameter, ripen in July and August. Found in old fields and along fencerows and woodland edges, Red Raspberry occurs throughout much of southern Ontario north into the Boreal Forest region.

FLOWERING RASPBERRY
(Rubus odoratus)

This species has rose-purple flowers, 3-5 cm across, and simple leaves with broadly triangular acute lobes. The leaves are usually 10-20 cm wide but occasionally up to 40 cm. Flowering occurs from late June to August, and the edible red fruit is up to 1 cm in diameter. The branches of the inflorescence, leaf stalks, and upper twigs are densely covered with gland-tipped hairs. Found along moist woodland edges and in clearings, Flowering Raspberry occurs in the Carolinian and southern Mixed Forest regions. Thimbleberry (*R. parviflorus*) is similar, but has white flowers, is less glandular-hairy, and has a more northerly distribution.

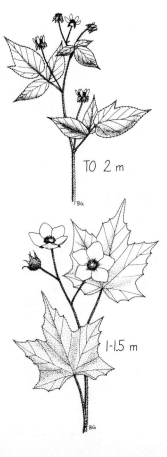

TO 2 m

1-1.5 m

(76)

COMMON BLACKBERRY
(Rubus allegheniensis)

Blackberries often have a solid white core, but when you pick a raspberry the receptacle remains attached to the fruit stalk, so that the red "berry" comes off with a hollow centre. The shrubby Blackberries have angular stems with stout, often broad-based thorns, and usually 5 palmately-compound leaflets on the first-year branches (primocanes). The white flowers of Common Blackberry, each 2-3 cm wide, appear in June. Found in open woods, woodland edges, and old fields, Common Blackberry occurs throughout southern Ontario north to the southern Mixed Forest region. The Smooth Blackberry (*R. canadensis*) is without glandular hairs and has a more northerly distribution.

DWARF BLACKBERRY
(Rubus pubescens)

Found throughout much of Ontario in damp woods and bogs, the Dwarf Blackberry becomes rare and local in the extreme south. A long, smooth, horizontal stem creeps over the soil surface, producing erect non-woody (herbaceous) stems, also without thorns or prickles. White flowers, 1-1.5 cm across, appear in clusters of 1-3 in late May and June. Dark red berries, 5-10 mm in diameter, ripen in July and August. Other trailing Blackberries, usually called Dewberries (*e.g. R. hispidus*), have upright stems that are woody and bristly. Stemless Dwarf Raspberry (*R. acaulis*) is found in damp woods and bogs in northern Ontario. It has several unarmed herbaceous stems, 5-10 cm high, arising from a short perennial base, and the flowers are pink.

CLOUDBERRY
(Rubus chamaemorus)

Simple leaves, to 9 cm wide with broadly rounded lobes, are borne on herbaceous unarmed stems. Large white solitary flowers, 2-3 cm wide, appear in June, and reddish fruits, 2 cm across, ripen to orange in July and August. To some the berries taste excellent, while to others they are like "insipid baked apples". Cloudberry occurs in Black Spruce–Sphagnum bogs in northern Ontario.

1-3 dm

(77)

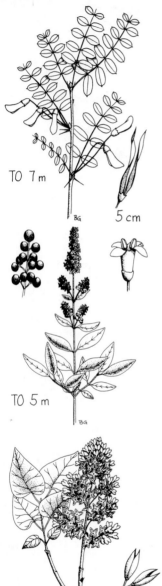

PEA TREE
(Caragana arborescens)

Pea Tree, introduced from Manchuria and Siberia, is grown as an ornamental and often used for hedges. It persists long after cultivation and has spread locally to meadows and wastelands. Yellow flowers (1.5-2.0 cm) appear on long stalks (3-6 cm) in late May and June. The stalks have a joint above the mid-point. Pea-like pods mature to a brown colour in late June and early July. They split lengthwise, each half twisting in a spiral. The oval leaflets, 1-2.5 cm, have bristle-tips. There is a pair of thorns at the base of each compound leaf.

COMMON PRIVET
(Ligustrum vulgare)

Introduced from Europe, Common Privet is a widely cultivated hedge plant. In parts of southern Ontario it has spread from cultivation to fields and woodlands. White flowers (5-7 mm long) are borne in dense clusters (3-6 cm) in June and July. The black shiny fruits, 6-8 mm across, ripen in September. Smooth leaves (3-6 cm long) stay green late in the fall, like those of so many other plants introduced from Europe.

COMMON LILAC
(Syringa vulgaris)

The showy flower clusters of Lilac, appearing in late May and early June, may be blue, purple, or white. Only Hyacinths match their fragrance. Individual flowers are 8-13 mm long and about 12 mm across. The corolla has 4 or sometimes 5 spreading lobes. Fruit capsules (10-12 mm long) containing 2 seeds in each of 2 compartments persist on the shrub, and those of the previous year are often present with the flowers. The leaves (5-12 cm) are flat or cordate at the base. A popular cultivated shrub, Lilac was introduced from Eurasia. It persists long after cultivation, and in some parts of southern Ontario it has escaped and is spreading.

(78)

WINTERBERRY
(Ilex verticillata)

Black Alder

The deciduous leaves have a wrinkled texture and are hairy on the veins below. Sometimes reaching 10 cm, they are mostly about 5 cm long. The secondary veins divide a few millimetres from the leaf margin. Small greenish to yellowish-white flowers, 4-6 mm across, are borne on short stalks (less than 5 mm) in the leaf axils during late June and July. They may occur singly or in dense clusters. The bright orange or reddish berry-like fruits, about 6 mm across, ripen in September and October and remain on the shrub through much of the winter. Where Winterberry is common, its bright berries produce a showy spectacle in an otherwise drab late autumn landscape. It may be found in swampy woods and along the edges of bogs and marshes from southern Ontario north to the southern Boreal Forest region. Winterberry is sometimes collected on a grand scale for Christmas decoration, and in some areas it has been seriously depleted. In New York and Michigan, it is protected from such devastation by state law. The "berries" of Winterberry and Christmas Holly, as well as those of Mistletoe, are poisonous.

BG TO 5 m

MOUNTAIN-HOLLY
(Nemopanthus mucronata)

Like Winterberry, this shrub is a deciduous member of the Holly family. The leaves (2-5 cm) are smooth-margined (or rarely with a few teeth) and lack prominent veins and hairs beneath. Mountain-holly may also be distinguished from Winterberry by the relatively long stalks on both flowers and fruits. The flowers, about 3 mm across, with 4 or 5 linear petals, are borne on stalks 10-25 mm long from the leaf axils. They appear in May and early June before the leaves have fully expanded. Reddish berry-like fruits about 6 mm across, on stalks 1-3 cm long, ripen in July and August. Mountain-holly occurs along the edges of bogs and swamps from southern Ontario (except the extreme south) north into the Boreal Forest region.

TO 3 m

BG

DOGWOODS

The Dogwood group includes small trees, shrubs, and herbaceous forms (see also pp. 65 and 118). Only the shrubs discussed below present difficulty in identification. These all have simple, smooth-margined, opposite leaves, with the veins curving toward the tip before reaching the margin, and small, whitish, 4-parted flowers in showy clusters. Branches are opposite. The distasteful berry-like fruits contain 1 or 2 seeds.

GREY DOGWOOD
(Cornus racemosa)

Distinctive features include the usually brownish pith in 2-4 year old branches, round-topped flower clusters and white fruits on bright red stalks. The leaves have 3-4 lateral veins on each side. The flowers, opening in late June, have petals 3-4 mm and are borne in clusters up to 3.5 cm high and 5 cm across (half to fully as high as wide). The 5-6 mm fruits ripen by late August. Found in open edge habitats, especially along fencerows, Grey Dogwood occurs throughout much of southern Ontario outside the Canadian Shield.

1-5 m

SILKY DOGWOOD
(Cornus amomum (C. obliqua))

Silky Dogwood has a brown pith in its 2-4 year old branches, dull-bluish fruits 6-8 mm on greenish stalks, and flat-topped flower clusters. The ovate leaves, with 3-5 veins on each side, often droop, and the youngest twigs have a dense greyish covering of light hairs quite unlike the smooth stems of Grey Dogwood. This is the latest-blooming native Dogwood, the flowers, with petals 4-5 mm, appearing in early July in more or less flat-topped clusters 3-5 cm across. Silky Dogwood is widespread in southern Ontario outside the Canadian Shield region, and is usually found in wet soil. (Until difficulty in separating *C. amomum* and *C. purpusi* is resolved in Ontario, we include the latter with *C. amomum*). The Rough-leaved Dogwood (*C. drummondii*) is similar to Silky Dogwood, but differs in having rough upper leaf surfaces and white fruits on purplish stalks. It is confined to the Carolinian zone.

1-3 m

RED OSIER DOGWOOD
(Cornus stolonifera)

Reddish-purple stems and branches with a white pith, a more or less flat-topped inflorescence, and white fruits characterize the Red Osier. The ovate leaves have 5-7 veins on each side. In October they turn bright pinkish, with the veins often remaining green. In winter the reddish-purple stems and twigs impart a bright warmth to a snowy landscape. The flowers appear mostly in late June, but a few clusters sometimes continue to appear throughout the summer. They are borne in more or less flat-topped clusters, 2-4 cm across, and have petals 3-5 mm long. Round, white, berry-like fruits, occasionally with a faint blue tinge, are about 6 mm across in August and September. Red Osier can spread by underground shoots, especially in moist sandy soils, and often produces extensive thickets. Cut branches placed in the soil will root and produce new plants, just as Willow and other wetland shrubs commonly do. Red Osier grows in swamps, along marsh edges and shores, and in moist places in general. It is common in southern Ontario, extending north to James Bay.

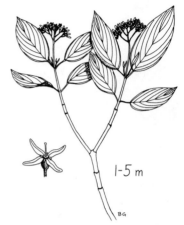

1-5 m

ROUND-LEAVED DOGWOOD
(Cornus rugosa)

Distinctive features of Round-leaved Dogwood include a white pith in the 2 to 4-year-old branches, flat-topped flower clusters, and blue or pale-blue fruits. In addition to its blue fruit, it differs from Red Osier Dogwood in its greenish or yellowish-green twigs and more broadly ovate or roundish leaves with 5-8 veins on each side. This attractive Dogwood has larger flower clusters than the other species, ranging from 3 to 7 cm across. The flowers open in late June, and the petals are 3-4 mm. The fruit, 5-6 mm, ripens in August and September. Round-leaved Dogwood is usually found in sandy or rocky limestone soils, where it occurs especially on steep slopes and in open woods. Its Ontario distribution includes the Carolinian and Mixed Forest regions.

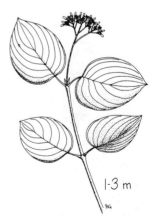

1-3 m

(81)

TO 3 dm

1.5 cm

1-2 m

TO 1 m

RUNNING STRAWBERRY-BUSH
(*Euonymus obovatus*)

A low creeping shrub with erect greenish branches, Running Strawberry-bush is generally inconspicuous among the other plants on the forest floor; but in September, when its unusual fruits ripen, it really catches the eye. The spiny 3-lobed capsules (1-1.5 cm) are pinkish or crimson and open to 2.5 cm) exposing orange to scarlet-coated seeds. The small greenish flowers (5-10 mm across) appear in late May and June. Smooth finely toothed leaves reach 8 cm in length. In Ontario, Running Strawberry-bush is confined to rich woodlands in the Carolinian zone. The closely related Burning Bush (*E. atropurpureus*), an erect shrub to 6 m with smooth 4-lobed fruits, is rare.

LEATHERWOOD
(*Dirca palustris*)

The brownish branches have enlarged nodes. The twigs are pliable and the bark is remarkably tough, giving rise to the popular name Leatherwood. Indians used the bark for cordage and basket making. The light-green leaves reach 10 cm. Pale yellow flowers (1 cm long) appear in April and May, when the leaves are still enclosed in brown hairy bud scales. Elliptical berry-like fruits (to 1.2 cm) ripen to a purplish-red by midsummer. Usually found in deciduous woodlands, Leatherwood occurs in the Carolinian and southern Mixed Forest regions of Ontario.

NEW JERSEY TEA
(*Ceanothus americanus*)

The prominently 3-ribbed leaves are 2.5 to 8 cm long. They are said to have been used as a substitute for tea in the United States during the War of Independence. Small white flowers (3 mm) appear in dense long-stemmed clusters from late June to early August. Three-lobed capsules (3-6 mm) have saucer-like bases which persist after the fruit is shed. New Jersey Tea is found in dry woods and clearings in southern Ontario. The less common Narrow-leaved New Jersey Tea (*C. herbaceus*) has narrowly elliptical leaves and shorter stalked flower clusters.

(82)

BUFFALO-BERRY
(Shepherdia canadensis)

The fruits contain a substance that foams in water, leading to the common name Soapberry. Though not a popular wild food with Europeans, the thick creamy "suds" produced by mixing the berries with water were considered a great delicacy by the Indians. The leaves (2-5 cm) are pale beneath with silvery star-shaped hairs and scattered brown scales. Small yellowish flowers (3-5 mm) appear before the leaves in April and May. The red or yellowish berry-like fruit (8 mm) ripens in July and August. Found on dry banks, on sand dunes, and in limestone areas, this shrub occurs from the Carolinian region north to the Hudson Bay Lowlands.

BUTTONBUSH
(Cephalanthus occidentalis)

The creamy flowers appear in July and August. They are 4-parted, tubular, and have protruding styles. Tightly packed in spherical heads (2-4 cm across), they contain much nectar and are visited by a large variety of insects. A spherical mass of nutlets matures in September and October. The thick leaves (to 18 cm long) are smooth and glossy above, pale and softly hairy below. Buttonbush occurs in damp places along streams, and at the edges of ponds and marshes, where it is sometimes found in shallow water. It appears to be confined in Ontario to the area south of 45° N., but is absent from the Algonquin upland.

BEARBERRY
(Arctostaphylos uva-ursi)

The reddish-brown postrate stems with papery peeling bark and short ascending branches are characteristic. Pink urn-shaped flowers (to 6 mm long) appear in dense terminal clusters in May and June. Inedible berry-like fruits (1 cm) are reddish. The firm evergreen leaves (1-3 cm) differ from those of Mountain Cranberry (p. 85); they have prominent veins below, are without bristle-like glands and are often broadest above the middle. Bearberry grows in open sandy or rocky places from the Carolinian zone north to the Hudson Bay tundra.

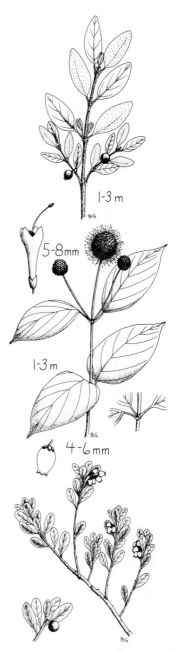

(83)

4-6 mm

TO 1 m

BLACK HUCKLEBERRY
(*Gaylussacia baccata*)

Black Huckleberries can be readily distinguished from Blueberries by their leaves. Huckleberry leaves are covered with golden yellow resinous dots, especially beneath. These dots are easily seen with a 10X magnifier. The pale yellowish or reddish flowers (to 6 mm) appear in May and June. Edible purplish-black berry-like fruits ripen in July and August. Black Huckleberry occurs in sandy and rocky acid soils and bogs throughout southern Ontario.

LOW SWEET BLUEBERRY
(*Vaccinium angustifolium*)

This is our commonest Blueberry, which ranges from the Carolinian zone north to the Boreal Forest region. It grows in acid sandy or shallow rocky soil in clearings and open woods. Distinctive features include the warty twigs, low stature, and minutely toothed leaves (2.5-4.5 cm) that are often paler beneath. Twigs and veins on the under surface of the leaf may be hairy, but the leaves are smooth above. The white or pale-pink 5-parted flowers, 6 mm long, appear with or before the leaves in May and early June. The sweet edible berries are blue with a whitish bloom. Pioneer farmers burned blueberry barrens once every five years to improve production.

The Low Sweet Blueberry differs from the Dry-Land Blueberry (*V. pallidum*) in having twigs with a whitish bloom and elliptical instead of ovate leaves. Dry-land Blueberry is rare and confined to the Carolinian zone in Ontario. The Deerberry (*V. stramineum*), to 1 m tall, also has a restricted Carolinian distribution in Ontario. It is without warty stems and the flowers and fruits have longer stalks. The flowers have a distinctive bell-shaped corolla with protruding stamens. The Highbush Blueberry (*V. corymbosum*), a larger crown-forming shrub to 3 m, with the larger leaves up to 7.5 cm long, is found in swamps and boggy areas in southern Ontario. There are three species of Bilberries in northern Ontario. These differ from Blueberries in having relatively smaller leaves, and flowers that are either solitary in the leaf axils or in small clusters of 2 or 3.

5-20 cm   5-7 mm

(84)

VELVET-LEAF BLUEBERRY
(Vaccinium myrtilloides)

This species differs from the Low Sweet Blueberry in having smooth-edged leaves that are densely hairy beneath and usually with at least some hair on the upper surface as well. The twigs are also velvety-hairy. It may be distinguished from hairy forms of Highbush Blueberry by its lower stature and smaller (4-6 mm) greenish-white to pinkish flowers, which appear in late May and June. Edible blue berries (6-9 mm) with a whitish bloom ripen in July and August. Velvet-leaf Blueberry occurs in sandy or rocky clearings, bogs, and swamps, throughout much of Ontario.

SMALL BOG CRANBERRY
(Vaccinium oxycoccus)

Creeping stems and persistent leathery leaves characterize the Cranberries. The Small Bog Cranberry has flower and fruit stalks with a pair of reddish scale-like bracts about 1.5 mm long attached below the middle of the stalk. The pointed ovate leaves (3-8 mm) have incurved edges and are dark green above and whitish below. Nodding pinkish flowers appear in June and July. The reddish berries, 6-8 mm across, ripen in August and September. Found in sphagnum bogs, the Small Bog Cranberry occurs throughout much of Ontario.

LARGE BOG CRANBERRY
(Vaccinium macrocarpon)

The flower and fruit stalks have a pair of greenish leaf-like bracts 2-4 mm long attached above the middle of the stalk. Ranging from 6-17 mm in length, the leaves are more oblong, less incurved on the underside and appear less pointed than those of *V. oxycoccus*. The pinkish flowers appear in June and July. Reddish berries 1-2 cm across ripen in September and October. This is the commercial Cranberry cultivated on Cape Cod, the New Jersey pine barrens bogs, and in parts of Wisconsin. It occurs in bogs and marshes throughout much of Ontario. The Mountain Cranberry (*V. vitis-idaea*) of northern Ontario also has red berries, creeping stems, and evergreen leaves, but the leaves are oval or elliptic, and black-dotted below.

2-4 dm

1-2 cm

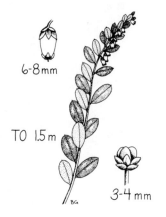

6-8 mm

TO 1.5 m

3-4 mm

LEATHER-LEAF
(Chamaedaphne calyculata)

Cassandra

Leather-leaf often comprises the dominant vegetation in open quaking bogs. In Ontario it extends from the Carolinian zone, where it is local, north into the Hudson Bay Lowlands. The evergreen leaves, 0.5-4.5 cm long, are green above and pale brownish beneath. Flowering occurs from late April to early June depending upon location. The whitish flowers (6 mm) are 5-parted and urn-shaped. They are pendant in the axils of smaller upper leaves. A roundish capsule, 3-4 mm across, with a persistent style, remains on the shrub after the numerous tiny seeds have been liberated.

TO 1 m

LABRADOR TEA
(Ledum groenlandicum)

With its younger branches and lower leaf surfaces densely woolly with whitish or brownish hair, the Labrador Tea is a very distinctive shrub. The evergreen leaves (2-5 cm) are smooth above. Evergreen plants are able to conserve vital nutrients such as nitrogen, which are scarce in the boggy substrate, and many of them are adapted to prevent water loss. Why? In winter no water can be absorbed from the frozen soil, so that if it is lost, it cannot be replaced. With their tough leathery texture, inrolled margins, and dense hair beneath, the leaves of Labrador Tea appear very well adapted. A tea made from these fragrant leaves is reported to be an effective treatment for coughs and colds. The creamy-white flowers (up to about 1 cm across) are borne on slender stalks in rounded terminal clusters (3-5 cm across). Flowering occurs from May to early July, when the pink flowers of orchids and laurels mingle with the abundant creamy clusters, making bog lands very colourful. The fruit is a slender capsule (about 5 mm long) containing numerous tiny seeds. Labrador Tea occurs in bogs and swamps, often in more shaded and somewhat drier sites than Leather-leaf. Its Ontario distribution extends from the Carolinian zone, where it is rare, north to Hudson Bay.

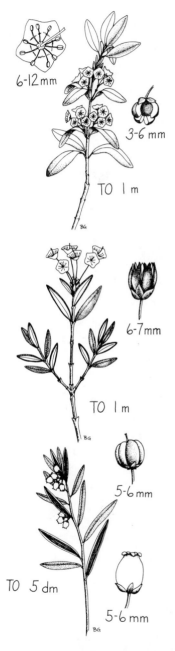

SHEEP-LAUREL
(Kalmia angustifolia)

Since it occasionally leads to the poisoning of livestock, this shrub is also called Lambkill. The showy pink flowers (6-12 mm across) appear in June and July in axillary clusters. The anthers are held in pockets of the corolla, and in response to the weight and disturbance of an insect visitor, they spring out dusting the insect with pollen. The evergreen leaves (2-5 cm) are smooth and pale below. Capsules (to 6 mm across) with persisting styles remain on the shrub after releasing numerous small seeds. Found in sphagnum bogs and open coniferous woods. Sheep-laurel is rare in the Carolinian region, becoming more common northward in the northern Mixed Forest and Boreal Forest regions.

BOG-LAUREL
(Kalmia polifolia)

Bog-laurel is distinguished from Sheep-laurel by its narrower stalkless leaves, usually with inrolled margins, winged (two-edged) instead of round stems, and terminal flower clusters. When flowers and fruit are not available, Bog-laurel may be confused with Bog-rosemary from which it differs in having opposite leaves and opposite two-edged twigs. The showy pink flowers (1-2 cm across) appear on long stalks in erect terminal clusters in May and June. Widespread in Ontario, Bog-laurel occurs in swamps and sphagnum bogs often with Leather-leaf and Bog Cranberries, but it is rare in the Carolinian zone.

BOG-ROSEMARY
(Andromeda glaucophylla)

The white or pink urn-shaped flowers about 6 mm long appear in drooping clusters in May and June. They are followed by a roundish many-seeded capsule (to 6 mm) with a persisting style. The leathery evergreen leaves 2.5-6 cm are whitened beneath and have inrolled edges. Found in sphagnum bogs, fens, and swamps. Bog-rosemary occurs from the Carolinian zone, where it is rare, north into the Hudson Bay Lowlands.

VIBURNUMS

The Viburnums have opposite branches, and opposite simple leaves which may be entire or lobed. The small 5-parted flowers are whitish and borne in dense clusters. In flower they might be confused with Dogwoods, which differ in having 4-parted flowers, and veins which curve toward the tip of the leaf before reaching the margin. Viburnums have fleshy or firm fruits with a single large flat stone.

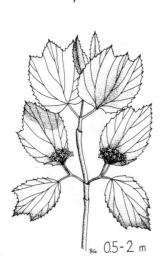

1-2 m

BG

MAPLE-LEAVED VIBURNUM
(*Viburnum acerifolium*)

One of our three Viburnums with maple-like leaves, this one differs from the others in having soft hairs covering the undersurface of the leaves. Under a 10X hand magnifier the hairs between the veins appear in star-shaped clumps (stellate) and the characteristic resin dots also show up well. In addition, this species produces fruits which become red but ripen to blue-black by late September. The small creamy-white flowers open in June, and are borne in clusters, 2.5 to 8 cm across. Leaves vary from 4 to 11 cm in length. Found in open woods, in thickets, and on slopes and banks, Maple-leaved Viburnum is confined to southern Ontario.

SQUASHBERRY
(*Viburnum edule*)

The leaves are without either resin dots or star-shaped clumps of hairs beneath, and the fruit, 6-12 mm in diameter, is at first yellow, ripening to orange or red during July and August. The Squashberry differs from Highbush Cranberry, in having no stipules at the base of the leaf stalks, and fewer flowers of only the small fertile type borne on short, two-leaved, lateral branches. The flowers are creamy-white and appear in June and early July in small clusters, about 2.5 cm across. The berries are less acid than those of Highbush Cranberry, and may be eaten raw or made into sauces and jellies. Squashberry occurs in damp woods, in swampy clearings, and along stream banks in the Boreal and northern Mixed Forest regions.

BG 0.5-2 m

(88)

HIGHBUSH CRANBERRY
(Viburnum opulus var. *americana)*

White flowers opening in June and July are borne in flat-topped clusters, to 15 cm across. Those around the edge of the cluster are sterile and have a greatly enlargened corolla, 1.5-3.5 cm across, while the flowers in the centre are fertile with corolla lobes only a few mm in length. Showy but sterile outer flowers are also characteristic of Hobblebush (below), and probably serve to attract pollinators. Highbush Cranberry is as attractive in fruit as it is in flower. The round juicy "berries", about 1 cm in diameter, ripen to bright orange-red by September and persist on the shrub throughout the winter. They have an acid but pleasant flavour and may be used in jellies. The bark has been used medicinally in the treatment of cramps, spasms, and mumps, accounting for the common name Crampbark. Highbush Cranberry occurs in moist open woods and woodland edges throughout much of Ontario. The introduced Guelder Rose (var. *opulus*), which sometimes escapes to natural habitats, differs in having concave disc-like glands on the upper leaf stalk rather than rounded projections. The cultivated Snowball Viburnum is closely related, but all its flowers are the showy sterile kind.

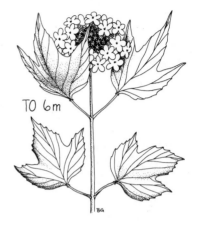

HOBBLEBUSH
(Viburnum alnifolium)

The large round leaves (10-20 cm) and sprawling habit are characteristic. Long straggling branches curve to the ground sometimes taking root and forming loops which trip the unwary, resulting in the common names Hobblebush, Witch Hobble, and Triptoe. Showy white flower clusters, up to 13 cm across, appear in late May and early June, with the larger sterile flowers, 2-3 cm across, around the edge. The fruit, up to 1 cm long, is red at first and becomes purplish-black by late summer. Found in damp woods, Hobblebush occurs in the southern part of the Mixed Forest region in Ontario, but is rare south of the Canadian Shield. The European Wayfaring Tree (*V. lantana*), which occasionally escapes from cultivation, is similar, but its leaves are longer than they are wide and the flower clusters lack the enlarged sterile flowers.

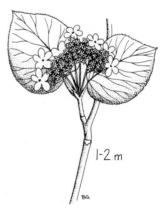

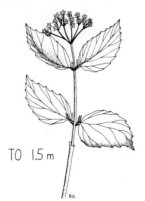

TO 1.5 m

DOWNY ARROW-WOOD
(Viburnum rafinesquianum)

Found in dry open woods and rocky (limestone) areas, the Downy Arrow-wood occurs in parts of southern Ontario outside the Canadian Shield region and locally in northern. Ontario. The coarsely-toothed leaves, 3-8.5 cm long, have short stalks usually less than 7 mm long and bristle-like stipules. The leaves are hairy beneath, and there are usually less than 11 teeth along each leaf edge. Creamy-white flowers appear in clusters 2-8 cm across in late May and early June. The elliptical fruits, dark purple to black and 6-9 mm long ripen in August and September.

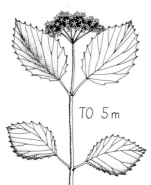

TO 5 m

SOUTHERN ARROW-WOOD
(Viburnum dentatum var. *lucidum)*

Unlike the preceding, this species is found in moist open woods and clearings. It is usually without stipules, and the coarsely toothed leaves, up to 10 cm long, often have more than 11 teeth along one side. The leaf stalks are usually more than 1 cm long, and the leaves are hairy only on the veins and vein axils below. Creamy-white flowers are borne in clusters, 5-9 cm across, in mid-June. Round to oval blue-black fruits, 6-9 mm long, ripen in August and September. Southern Arrow-wood is confined to southern Ontario, where it is local.

TO 4 m

WILD RAISIN
(Viburnum cassinoides)

Wild Raisin is a distinctive Viburnum with entire or wavy-toothed (never sharp-toothed) leaves, 4-10 cm long. The creamy-white flowers open in late June and are carried in clusters 5-10 cm across. Round or elliptical bluish or blue-black fruits, 6-9 mm long, ripen in August or September and have a thin but sweet pulp. Wild Raisin is found in moist acid soil of swamps, bog edges, and shores throughout much of Ontario north to the southern Boreal Forest region. It is rather local in southern Ontario south of the Canadian Shield. (See also *V. lentago*, p. 55.)

FRAGRANT SUMAC
(Rhus aromatica)

Fragrant Sumac occurs in dry sandy or rocky (usually limestone) places. Although widespread in southern Ontario, it is essentially absent from the Canadian Shield region. The three leaflets remind one of Poison Ivy, but unlike Poison Ivy the terminal leaflet is not stalked and the fruits are hairy and reddish. The flowers appear in late April, May, or early June, before the leaves are fully expanded. They are small (2 mm long), yellow, and are borne in dense spikes (about 1 cm long). The fruits (4-8 mm) ripen in late July and August. The leaves are fragrant when crushed.

COMMON ELDER
(Sambucus canadensis)

The pinnately compound leaves have 5-11 leaflets 5 to 15 cm long. The white flowers (4-7 mm) are borne in more or less flat-topped clusters 10-17 cm across, which are characteristically wider than long and are without an obvious central axis. The flowers open in July and August. Purplish-black berry-like fruits up to 6 mm across ripen in September. The warty greyish-brown twigs have a white pith. Found in moist open woods and clearings, Common Elder occurs from the Carolinian zone to the Mixed Forest region. The berries of this species are edible and can be used to make wine, but those of the following species are not edible, and the roots, stems, and leaves of both Elders are reported to be poisonous.

RED-BERRIED ELDER
(Sambucus pubens)

This species differs from the Common Elder in having an elongate flower cluster with a well developed central axis, inedible red fruit, and twigs with a brown pith. The white flowers, borne in clusters 4 to 12 cm long, appear in May and June, well before those of Common Elders growing nearby. The fruits ripen from mid-July to August. Red-berried Elder occurs in open woods from the Carolinian zone north to James Bay.

(91)

.25-1m

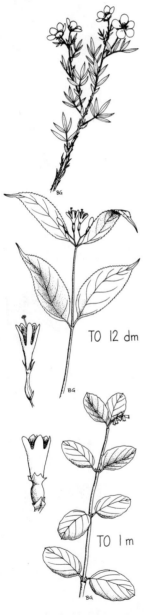

SHRUBBY CINQUEFOIL
(Potentilla fruticosa)

The palmately lobed leaves 1-3 cm long are covered with silky whitish hairs beneath. With such distinctive foliage and bright-yellow 5-parted flowers, 2-3 cm across, the Shrubby Cinquefoil is unmistakable. Flowering usually occurs in July and August, but may begin in June and continue until October. The older bark is reddish-brown and shreddy. Although widespread in Ontario from the Carolinian zone to the tundra, this shrub is not common throughout and occurs mainly in lime-rich soils in fens, on limestone plains, and along shorelines. (See also p. 133.)

BUSH HONEYSUCKLE
(Diervilla lonicera)

Characteristic of dry and more or less open locations, Bush Honeysuckle extends from the Carolinian zone to the southern Boreal Forest region. Its leaves, 8-15 cm, differ from those of other Honeysuckles in having toothed margins. The tubular 5-parted flowers, 1 to 1.5 cm long, open mostly in June and July. They are borne in short-stalked clusters and are at first pale yellow, but later turn reddish. The fruit is a slender pointed capsule up to about 1 cm in length, with the calyx lobes persisting as 5 bristles at the tip.

TO 12 dm

SNOWBERRY
(Symphoricarpos albus)

The small pink and white flowers (6 mm long) are tubular and 5-parted. They are borne in clusters of up to 5. Flowering occurs mostly in June and July. Round white berries, 6-10 mm across, ripen in August and September. The shreddy older bark and the opposite oval leaves which are hairy beneath are also good identification features. Snowberry grows in open woods and clearings from the Carolinian zone north to James Bay. A taller variety (*laevigata*) with smooth leaves, more abundant flowers, and larger fruits occasionally escapes from cultivation. The Wolf Berry (*S. occidentalis*) is similar but less common. It may be distinguished by its longer hairy style (4-7 mm) and later flowering season (July and August).

TO 1m

(92)

HONEYSUCKLES

These shrubs have smooth-margined opposite leaves with short stalks, and tubular 5-parted flowers. The fruit is a several-seeded berry which may be red, orange, purplish, or blue. Four of the Ontario species are not illustrated. The vine-like Hairy Honeysuckle (*L. hirsuta*), reaching 3 m, is similar to *L. dioica* but the leaves are hairy on both sides. It occurs in open woods. Mountain Fly Honeysuckle (*L. villosa*), reaching 1 m tall, has short-stalked (13 mm or less) flowers and fruits. It occurs in bogs and clearings from southern Ontario to James Bay, but is not common. Swamp Fly Honeysuckle (*L. oblongifolia*), is much like *L. canadensis*, but flowers later and has hairy undersides to the leaves. It is widespread but local in fens and swamps. Bracted Honeysuckle (*L. involucrata*), with green or purplish bracts (1.5 cm) subtending the flowers, and oval leaves to 15 cm, is common in the Boreal Forest.

WILD HONEYSUCKLE
(Lonicera dioica)

Yellow, orange, or red flowers, 1.5-3 cm long, appear from late May to early July. The leaves, reaching 11 cm, are smooth above and whitish below. Occurs in lime-rich soils of open woods and clearings from the Carolinian zone north to James Bay.

FLY HONEYSUCKLE
(Lonicera canadensis)

The pale-yellow flowers (to 2 cm long) appear in May and early June before the leaves have fully expanded. Leaves (to 9 cm) are smooth. Found in woodlands and swamps from the Carolinian zone north to the southern Boreal Forest region.

TARTARIAN HONEYSUCKLE
(Lonicera tatarica)

This Eurasian species has escaped from cultivation especially in southern Ontario. The pink or white flowers (1-2 cm long) appear in May and June. It occurs in open woods, woodland edges, and old fields.

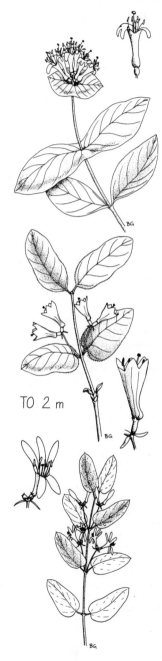

TO 2 m

(93)

VINES

POISON IVY
(Rhus radicans)

"Leaflets three, let it be." "Berries white, take flight." You can live without knowing these two rhymes, but you may suffer considerable discomfort. A severe skin irritation, in the form of small watery blisters, may result from contact with this plant. It is possible to contract the rash at any time of year, but it occurs most commonly in spring and early summer when the plant tissue is very soft and easily bruised, and the unwary may come into direct contact with an oily chemical in the plant sap. Sensitivity to Poison Ivy varies from one person to another, and may even change during your lifetime: because you were immune last year may not mean that you will be immune next year. If you have touched Poison Ivy, wash your hands with soap and water as soon as possible. Clothes should also be washed, since the oil remains active for a long time. The sap of Jewel-weed (p. 146) applied to the skin is reputed to decrease or eliminate the reaction, but once contracted many people find that there is nothing more soothing to the rash than a hot bath.

In June, compact clusters of yellowish-green 5-parted flowers are borne in the leaf axils. The hard berry-like fruits (5-6 mm) are greenish-yellow in August and September, but turn white and remain on their stalks throughout the winter. The leaves may turn yellow to crimson in the fall. Poison Ivy has a variety of growth forms. It may be a creeping plant to 30 cm tall, spreading by underground roots, and appearing herb-like. Sometime it is a woody sprawling shrub to 1 m tall. In parts of the Carolinian zone, it often occurs as a massive woody vine with aerial roots, climbing high into the tree tops. Poison Ivy occurs in swamps, meadows, and open woods in southern Ontario, but is rare in the northern parts of the Mixed Forest region. The plant is little discouraged by most chemical weed killers, although these effectively destroy nearby wildflowers. It is dangerous to burn Poison Ivy, since droplets of the oil are dispersed on smoke particles, and severe attacks may result from inhalation. But this vine does have its place in the balance of nature: the berries are eaten by many kinds of birds, and the stems and leaves are browsed by mammals and used as food and shelter by various insects.

CLIMBING BITTERSWEET
(Celastrus scandens)

This twining plant with finely toothed leaves (5-10 cm) may have woody trunks up to 2.5 cm thick. The small 5-parted greenish-white flowers appear in terminal clusters in May and June. When ripe, the orange berry-like capsules split into 3 sections and expose the seeds, each 6 mm in diameter and covered with bright-red tissue. These colourful showy fruits are often used in dry bouquets, but they should be kept away from children since they are poisonous. Watch for Bittersweet along river banks and woodland edges in the Carolinian and Mixed Forest regions.

PURPLE CLEMATIS
(Clematis verticillaris)

The purplish flowers (5-7.5 cm across) open in May and have showy translucent sepals. Petals are inconspicuous. The blossoms are solitary in the axils of long-stalked leaves. By midsummer the grey feathery styles produce silvery plumed fruiting heads. The plant climbs by bending its leaf stalks for support. Purple Clematis grows on rocky slopes and in open woods or thickets in the Mixed Forest zone. Virgin's Bower (*C. virginiana*) has smaller white flowers in branched axillary clusters. It occurs in the Carolinian as well as in the Mixed Forest region.

VIRGINIA CREEPER
(Parthenocissus quinquefolia)

Turning bright red in autumn, the palmately compound leaves of this woody climber trail over the forest floor and up tree trunks. Found mainly in the Carolinian zone, this plant has dull leaves, branched flower clusters with a central axis, bluish-black berries 5-7 mm across, and adhesive discs at the ends of the branched tendrils. Another Virginia Creeper, (*P. inserta*), has a more northern distribution, growing in the Mixed Forest as well as the Carolinian zone. It differs in having shiny leaves, fewer flowers in a more spreading inflorescence without a central stalk, fruits 8-10 mm, and no adhesive discs. Both species flower in June, and their fruits appear in August.

(95)

CARRION-FLOWER
(Smilax herbacea)

During May and June the rounded umbels of 20-100 flowers produce a very unpleasant odour much like decaying flesh. The umbels are on long stalks, which come from the axils of the leaves. Greenish or yellowish 6-parted flowers (3-4 mm long) are either male or female. Later, bluish-black berries with a bloom are produced in dense heads. Carrion-flower is without woody growth or bristles. The simple alternate leaves have a distinctive vein pattern and are yellowish-green with very pale, almost whitish, under surfaces. Tendrils at the ends of the stipules help the plant to climb. Found in open woods, thickets, and meadows, Carrion-flower occurs in the Carolinian and Mixed Forest regions.

BRISTLY GREENBRIER
(Smilax hispida)

The Bristly Greenbrier differs from the Carrion-flower (above) in being a woody perennial which has numerous bristles and prickles on the stems. Flowering occurs from mid-May to early July, but no foul odour is produced. It is often found clambering over bushes and taller herbs. Bristly Greenbrier is similar to Carrion-flower in its habitat and Ontario distribution.

CANADA MOONSEED
(Menispermum canadense)

In June and July, Canada Moonseed has axillary branched clusters of small white flowers; in September, it has black "berries" with a whitish bloom. It differs from Riverbank Grape (opposite) in having untoothed leaves which vary from circular to 3-7 lobed. The leaf stalks of Moonseed are twisted, and instead of being attached directly to the base of the leaf, they are joined a few millimetres away from the edge to the under surface of the blade. The 1-seeded fruits (6-10 mm) have a crescent-shaped flattened stone inside, rather than several circular seeds as in grapes. The fruit of Moonseed is poisonous. This vine grows in rich thickets and along stream banks in the Carolinian zone and parts of the southern Mixed Forest region.

(96)

WILD CUCUMBER
(Echinocystis lobata)

From June to October this high-climbing annual bears clusters of white 6-parted (male) flowers (1-1.5 cm). The 1-3 nodding female flowers are borne in the same leaf axils as the ascending male inflorescences. The fruit is a fleshy inflated bladder, 3-5 cm long, covered with weak prickles, and containing 4 seeds. The long-stalked leaves have 3 or 5 triangular lobes. Three-branched tendrils are opposite the leaves and form tight elastic coils. With similar but less prominently lobed leaves, Bur Cucumber *(Sicyos angulatus)* has 5-parted flowers and clusters of smaller (15 mm) 1-seeded fruits on long stalks. Both species grow in moist places in the Carolinian and Mixed Forest regions.

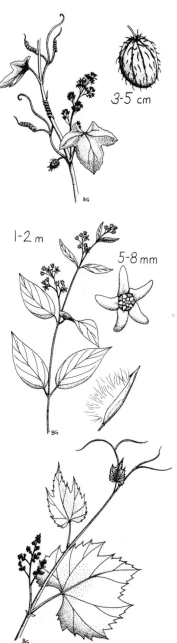

BLACK SWALLOW-WORT
(Vincetoxicum medium)

This non-woody perennial becomes a twining vine when the stems have grown tall enough. The small fragrant purple flowers occur in axillary clusters, and the slender pods become 4.5-8 cm long. Closely related to Milkweed, Black Swallow-wort has similar fruits; its silky hairs, attached to the seeds, aid in wind dispersal. A relatively recent introduction from Europe, it is rapidly spreading through open fields and meadows in southern Ontario.

RIVERBANK GRAPE
(Vitis riparia)

Riverbank Grape is a high-climbing woody vine found along river banks and in rich thickets in the Carolinian and Mixed Forest regions, mainly off the Canadian Shield. The small 5-parted flowers occur in branched axillary clusters (to 12 cm) from mid-May to early July. By September, juicy blue-black berries 8-12 mm in diameter have a heavy whitish bloom and an acid taste; they contain up to 4 seeds. Tendrils occur opposite the 3-lobed roundish coarsely-toothed leaves (7-15 cm). Sometimes shrubs or small trees are completely covered by wild grapes. The fruits are often used in jellies, but will make your mouth pucker up if you try them raw.

(97)

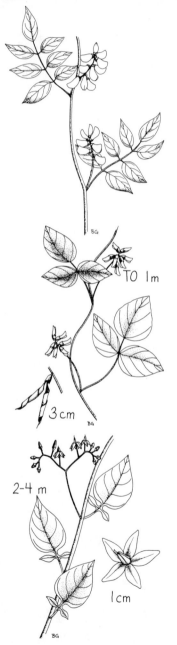

GROUND NUT
(*Apios americana*)

The slender soft stems of the Ground Nut twine and climb over vegetation close to the ground. In August, fragrant purple-brown Sweet Pea-like flowers occur in dense clusters on long stalks from the leaf axils. Fruits are similar to small bean pods. The alternate leaves have 5-9 short-stalked leaflets. The root has a chain of tuber-like thickenings (2.5-7.5 cm long) similar to a string of beads. An attempt was made to cultivate them as a substitute for potatoes, but growth was too slow. Ground Nut occurs in thickets and moist open woods in the Carolinian zone and the southern Mixed Forest.

HOG PEANUT
(*Amphicarpa bracteata*)

Delicate twining stems covered with brownish hairs support the 3 finely hairy leaflets (2-6 cm) of the alternate leaves. Pale violet or white pea-like flowers are borne in axillary clusters in August and produce 3-seeded pods which coil apart at maturity. Flowers without petals occur on slender runners at or near the base of the stem, and produce small fleshy 1-seeded pods. Hog Peanuts grow in moist thickets and woods in the Carolinian and Mixed Forest regions, mainly south of the Canadian Shield.

BITTERSWEET NIGHTSHADE
(*Solanum dulcamara*)

This introduced woody climber has been very successful in thickets, clearings, and even backyards. From mid-May to September, flower clusters are at first terminal but as the stem grows they become lateral and occur in the internodes between the leaves. The 5 purple petals are swept back from a cone of projecting yellow stamens. The green berries (8-11 mm) ripen to a red colour. Black Nightshade (*S. nigrum*) is a bushy annual plant with blunt-toothed or almost entire leaves. The flowers are similar in shape to those of the Bittersweet Nightshade, but the petals are white. Round black berries are 8 mm across. The berries of both species are poisonous, at least when young.

Common Wildflowers

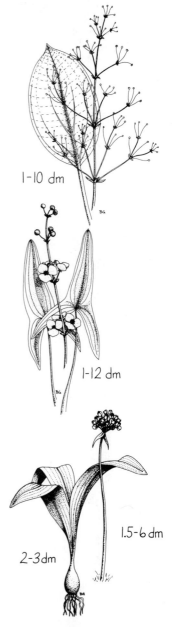

WATER PLANTAIN
(Alisma plantago-aquatica)

In the mud along the margins of slow-moving streams, around ponds and in marshes, these semi-aquatics send their tall stalks above the water and beyond the leaves, producing an open inflorescence of tiny white 3-petalled flowers. Found throughout Ontario, they bloom from June to September. Each flower produces a circular green fruiting head, with each of the many pistils maturing into a flattened achene with ribs on the back. The leaf shape and vein pattern remind you of the weedy Common Plantain.

1-10 dm

BROAD-LEAVED ARROWHEAD
(Sagittaria latifolia)

Often found with the Water Plantain in muddy shallow water habitats, the Arrowhead has much larger flowers, a less branched inflorescence, and its leaves look like the tips of arrows. Its leaf stalks (petioles) are usually as long as the water is deep, so that the leaf blades are held above the water surface. The showy flowers, generally either male or female, occur in groups of 3 from July to September. The leaf shape varies from broad to very narrow. This is the most common of several species in our area. The starchy tubers were a popular food among Indians from coast to coast.

1-12 dm

WILD LEEK
(Allium tricoccum)

In early spring, this is one of the first and most commonly seen plants in Deciduous and Mixed Forest woodlands. In patches here and there, the broad lily-like leaves form a dense cover of green, and when a leaf is crushed underfoot, the aroma of onions fills the air. Taking advantage of the spring growth period, when there is still lots of sunshine reaching the forest floor, the wild leek leaves have often turned yellow by the time the trees have fully leafed out and by early June they have disappeared. Later in June and July, solitary stalks, each holding a white "pom-pom", emerge mysteriously from the leaf duff, looking very much like onion flower-heads and made up of many small 6-parted flowers.

2-3 dm

1.5-6 dm

FALSE SOLOMON'S SEAL
(Smilacina racemosa)

This late spring lily blooms in rich woods in May and June. A cluster of tiny flowers terminates a gently arching stem. Each flower is 6-parted, and the petals and sepals look the same. In summer, the brownish striped berries become translucent red. The stem zigzags between each of the alternate short-petioled leaves. These look similar to the leaves of the true Solomon's Seal, which is readily distinguished by its bell-like yellowish flowers. Of the 3 species of *Smilacina* in Ontario, *S. racemosa* is the most commonly encountered.

STARRY FALSE SOLOMON'S SEAL
(Smilacina stellata)

Shorter than the above, but with fewer and larger flowers, this close relative grows in moist open places or on sandy ground (especially dunes) along the Great Lakes. It blooms from May to July. The pale-green leaves with their parallel vein pattern clasp the zigzagging stem. An open colony is often produced, since the rhizomes branch freely and send out new erect or slightly arching shoots. The berries are deep red at maturity, but are speckled or striped while developing. The even smaller Bog Solomon's Seal (*S. trifolia*) occurs in wet woods or bogs. Its 2 or 3 leaves almost sheath the stem and it has a more open raceme.

CANADA MAYFLOWER
(Maianthemum canadense)

In May and June in moist or dry woods you will surely see this wildflower forming patches at the base of a beech, maple, or hemlock. It does well in the shade of the young canopy and continues to grow when many of the earlier spring flowers have yellowed and disappeared. It is our only lily with 4-parted flowers; all the rest have 3-parted flowers. By July speckled berries have been produced which eventually become pale red when mature. In most of the plants you find, the backs of the two heart-shaped sessile leaves will be hairless, but in drier sandy woods a variety with a downy covering on the backs of the leaves may be found.

WHITE TRILLIUM
(Trillium grandiflorum)

Our provincial floral emblem since 1937, the White Trillium was chosen partly for its graceful appearance and simple structure; it was considered to be a blossom of peace, and associated with the gladness, beauty, and fresh hope of spring. Most abundant in the rich deciduous forests of southern Ontario, it becomes less frequent northward. The white petals often turn flush pink toward the end of the flowering season in May. Flowers with petals either completely green or streaked with green are caused by minute bacteria-like organisms.

2-4 dm

PAINTED TRILLIUM
(Trillium undulatum)

It is a delight to find the Painted Trillium, with its red blaze at the base of each white wavy-edged petal. Watch for it during May or June in acid woods and swamps. Its leaves are a distinctive dark bluish-green. Most common in the Canadian Shield region, it is seldom seen southward. Extending even farther north, and rare south of the Canadian Shield, the Nodding Trillium (*T. cernuum*) can be identified by its white flowers which hang below the leaves. Later it produces 6-lobed red berries, while those of the Painted Trillium are 3-lobed.

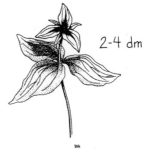

2-4 dm

NODDING LADIES'-TRESSES
(Spiranthes cernua)

This species is one of the most common and adaptable orchids in southern Ontario. It differs from several close relatives in having larger (1 cm) and pure crystalline-white flowers. Look for it at the end of August and during September in open moist soil. It is not infrequent in roadside ditches in Muskoka and is a part of the final autumn show in the shoreline meadows around the lower Great Lakes, commonly occurring with Grass of Parnassus, Fringed Gentian, Kalm's Lobelia, and Purple Gerardia. The spiral twisted spike of delicate blossoms has been likened to braided hair or curls.

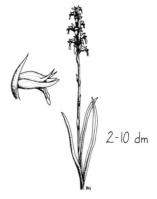

2-10 dm

(101)

WILD ASPARAGUS
(*Asparagus officinalis*)

Certainly not one of our prettiest wildflowers, but very tasty, this European species has escaped from cultivation and spread widely, perhaps through the efficient dispersal of its red berries by birds in the fall. In spring, when the young shoots look like spears emerging from the ground, they can be picked as a vegetable. Although difficult to spot the young shoots, the tall freely branching skeletons of last year's stalks may help you locate them. It is interesting that the feathery fern-like "leaves" of the mature plant are in reality modified branches; the true leaves themselves have been reduced to very tiny scales.

PROSTRATE KNOTWEED
(*Polygonum aviculare*)

A European introduction, frequent in lawns, playing fields, and waste ground, this prostrate or low annual can withstand much trampling. It is often found along pathways and encroaching upon cement sidewalks. On close inspection, tiny white flowers, rimmed with pink, can be seen in the axils of the bluish-green leaves. The stems are swollen where the leaves are attached and thus appear jointed or knotted.

BUCKWHEAT
(*Fagopyrum esculentum*)

Spreading from or persisting after cultivation, this Asian plant may be found in waste places, along roadsides, in the cinders along a railway, or in old fields. The flower clusters are composed of many white-sepalled tiny blossoms which eventually give rise to 3-sided fruits or "grains". The swollen sheaths along the stem and the arrow-shaped leaves might lead to confusion with several similar vine-like members of the knotweed group, which are distinguished by their slender spike-like racemes with fewer, often greenish, flowers. The Black Bindweed (*Polygonum convolvulus*), which is also a weedy introduction, usually has 2 leaves per node, one often quite small, and the flowers are in the leaf axils.

NARROW-LEAVED SPRING BEAUTY
(Claytonia virginica)

The candy-cane flowers, white with pink stripes, readily distinguish this early spring wildflower. It becomes rare outside the rich deciduous woods of the Carolinian zone and is largely replaced in the southern parts of the Mixed Forest by the Wide-leaved Spring Beauty (*C. caroliniana*), which has broad blunt leaves with long tapering petioles (illustrated on far right). In the western Lake Ontario and the southern Niagara Escarpment regions one can sometimes find a wood in which both species grow together, but such situations are unusual.

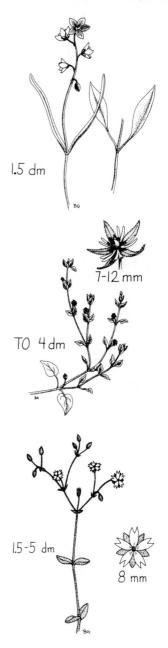

1.5 dm

COMMON CHICKWEED
(Stellaria media)

This Eurasian species is one of the most common weeds of lawns, though it also grows in waste places, fields, and even damp woods, trailing over the ground, often forming mats. Since it remains green beneath the snow, by March you can usually find open flowers in the axils of the upper leaves, for it is one of the first city plants to bloom in the spring. The 5 petals, which are shorter than the sepals, are so deeply divided it looks as if there are really 10. Long known to the herbalists, this tiny plant is extremely useful. An excellent source of vitamin C, it can be cooked or eaten raw in a salad with tangy greens. It has been used as an external poultice, and is even said to be a remedy for obesity.

7-12 mm

TO 4 dm

COMMON MOUSE-EAR CHICKWEED
(Cerastium vulgatum)

Another introduced species, this one does amazingly well in a disturbed setting such as along a roadside, in a field, or in some other cultivated area. It is a taller plant than the Common Chickweed, with hairy sessile leaves and much broader petals that are only notched to about half their length. Flowering continues from early spring to late fall. Field Chickweed (*C. arvense*) is a variable species which grows mainly on gravelly or rocky alkaline soils. It has larger flowers, narrower leaves, and its sepals are only half the length of the petals.

1.5-5 dm

8 mm

2-8 dm

4-12 dm

4-8 dm

BLADDER CAMPION
(Silene vulgaris (S. cucubalis))

The smooth pale pink or green balloon-like calyx sacs will help you spot this Eurasian plant which flourishes along roadsides and in fields. With more slender and hairy calyx sacs, the Night Flowering Catchfly (*S. noctiflora*), is often a troublesome weed and is frequently confused with the White Cockle. Its fragrant flowers open at night, and the internodes of the stem produce a sticky substance which traps airborne material and insects. With slightly narrower leaves, very short petals, and a more upright inflorescence, the native Sleepy Catchfly (*S. antirrhina*) is found in dry, open, often disturbed sites. In all these species flowering extends from June to September.

WHITE COCKLE
(Silene alba (Lychnis alba))

Sometimes this Eurasian biennial or short-lived perennial is confused with the Night Flowering Catchfly, which is an annual. Although both are hairy, the most obvious distinguishing feature is the stickiness of the Catchfly. The Cockle differs also in having broader and larger petals that are less deeply notched, a taller stature, only male or female (imperfect) flowers, and stigmas with 5 styles rather than 3. It is not as serious a weed in cultivated fields as the Catchfly, and is not as common in the north.

SOAPWORT
(Saponaria officinalis)

Yet another member of the Pink family from the Old World, this leafy perennial is very common along roadsides and railway embankments, around old buildings, and in fields and pastures. The showy clusters of typically white flowers with slender sepal tubes are very distinctive. After the pollen has been shed, the petals (which may also be pink) bend back toward the stem, making the 2 styles more obvious. At least 3 lengthwise veins line the smooth opposite leaves. Because the plant contains a juice which lathers in water, early settlers used it as an effective substitute for soap.

FRAGRANT WATER-LILY
(Nymphaea odorata)

To come upon a quiet stream or pond in early morning, when the exquisite blossoms of this lily are filling the air with their beautiful fragrance, is a rare treat. Long slender stalks join the floating flowers and leaves to the rhizome buried in the mud. The almost circular leaves, which act as support for all kinds of living things both above and below the water, are usually purplish on their under surface. Beginning in June, flowering continues through the summer. Numerous bright-yellow stamens contrast with the snow-white petals. Another species, *N. tuberosa*, is also found here, but has no fragrance; it has more rounded petal tips, and the leaf under surface is usually green.

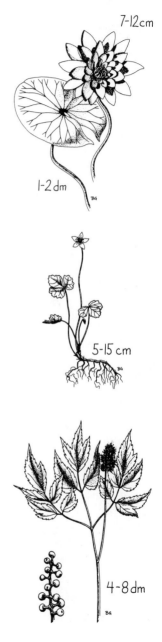

7-12cm

1-2dm

GOLDTHREAD
(Coptis trifolia)

Each pure white star-like flower is held above the leaves on slender leafless stalks and can be seen in moist woods, swamps, or bogs from late May to early July. More widespread in the north, in the extreme southern parts of the province, Goldthread is usually found in mossy coniferous woods that are colder than normal. The shiny dark-green leaves are divided into 3 toothed segments and resemble tiny evergreen strawberry leaves. They are attached to the golden thread-like rhizomes by thin petioles.

5-15 cm

WHITE BANEBERRY
(Actaea alba)

This member of the Buttercup family is just as attractive in fruit as it is in flower. It can be found blooming in rich woods in the Deciduous and Mixed Forest regions during May and early June. By August, the showy white berries on thick red stalks have a black spot and are sometimes called "Doll's Eyes". Another species, Red Baneberry (*A. rubra*), very similar at flowering time, produces shiny red berries held on delicate thin stalks; this species extends into the Boreal Forest. Look for intermediates between these two species. A white-berried form of Red Baneberry, found less frequently farther south, is more common beyond the range of White Baneberry.

4-8dm

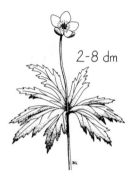

CANADA ANEMONE
(Anemone canadensis)

2-8 dm

Found throughout much of Ontario in damp thickets, in meadows, and along gravelly shores, this Anemone blossoms from late May to July. Each flower, with its 5 petal-like sepals, rises above a circle of stalkless leaves. The fruiting head is circular, whereas that of the Thimbleweed (*A. virginiana*), of dry open woods, is long and thimble-like, while the petals are less showy and the divided leaflets are stalked. The Long-headed Anemone (*A. cylindrica*) can be distinguished by its even longer fruit head (to 4 cm), and leaf stalks as long as the blades; it grows best on dry open areas or slopes. The light fluffy seeds of these species are dispersed by wind.

WOOD ANEMONE
(Anemone quinquefolia)

1-2 dm

This delicate woodland plant flowers in spring and early summer, prefers moist shady sites, and is widespread in Ontario. Although real petals are absent, 4-9 (usually 5) sepals appear petal-like. The 3 leaf blades are so deeply cut that sometimes it looks as if there are 5. Unlike its relatives described above, it is completely without hairs on the stem or leaves, and is also much smaller; however, it does have many stamens and pistils and 1 flower per stem, just like the other anemones.

ACUTE-LOBED HEPATICA
(Hepatica acutiloba)

5-15 cm

In early spring, here and there through the maple-beech woods, when only the leaves of the Leek and Trout Lily are beginning to show green, tiny bouquets of delicate white, pink, blue, or purple flowers of the Hepatica greet the woodland traveller. Last year's leaves, looking a little the worse for wear, are still green, and were able to use the autumn sunlight after the leaves of the forest canopy had been shed. Round-lobed Hepatica (*H. americana*) with more rounded leaf lobes, usually occurs in drier acid soil of oak woodlands. Hepatica refers to the liver, and the resemblance of the leaves to this organ led to the medieval belief that the plant could cure liver disorders.

(106)

MAY-APPLE
(*Podophyllum peltatum*)

Big patches of umbrella-shaped leaves first draw one's attention to these plants. When emerging from the ground in early spring, the flower bud looks like a nodding head between two strong shoulders which become the leaves. Not until later in May do the waxy 6-9 petalled flowers open on their arching stalks beneath the leaves. By mid-summer, a large lemon-like berry is produced, which can be used to prepare jams and marmalades. However, the root and foliage, as well as green fruits, are poisonous and should not be eaten.

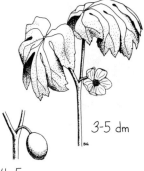

3-5 dm

4-5 cm

TWINLEAF
(*Jeffersonia diphylla*)

The two opposite leaves, looking like the wings of a butterfly, distinguish this early spring wildflower which is essentially confined to the Carolinian zone. In April or May you can find the fragile solitary blossoms that remind you of Bloodroot, standing tall and leafless, but the distinctive leaf shape and the bluish-green rather than yellowish-green colour indicate that it is indeed Twinleaf. By June the leaves have enlarged and become deep green. The maturing capsules open horizontally at about the middle, the upper part becoming a lid. Twinleaf grows in clumps at the base (or partly up the slopes) of river valleys, often with the White Trout Lily.

1-2 dm

BLOODROOT
(*Sanguinaria canadensis*)

This is traditionally one of the wildflowers that heralds the arrival of spring. The delicate white flowers appear in April in woodlands of the Deciduous and Mixed Forest regions. Often growing in clumps, solitary flowers on long stalks are surrounded by pale-green lobed leaves. All too soon the 8-12 petals gently fall to the ground, leaving the slender ovary. By late spring the leaves have grown to about twice their size and overtop the elongated capsules. North American Indians used the bright orange-red sap produced by the plant as a skin dye.

5-15 cm

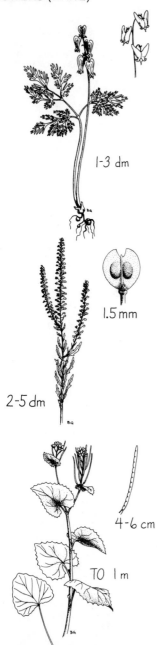

DUTCHMAN'S BREECHES
(Dicentra cucullaria)

In rich deciduous woodlands in southern Ontario you sometimes come across small patches of this dainty wildflower. The waxy cream flowers look like miniature Dutchmen from the folk tales, wearing baggy pantaloons, turned upside-down and suspended from an arching stalk. Each of the "legs" is actually a spur of a petal which contains nectar to attract insects. The pale greenish-blue leaves are very fragile in appearance and much dissected. A cluster of small white tubers gives rise to the flower stalk and leaves. In the closely related Squirrel Corn (*D. canadensis*), the tubers are yellow, resembling grains of Indian corn, and the whitish or pinkish flower has spurs that are shorter and rounded (illustrated on the far left).

PEPPERGRASS
(Lepidium densiflorum)

Along roadways, paths, or bare ground in vacant lots in the city, and commonly in cultivated fields, you will see this introduced weed. From June to August its dense ascending raceme, with small rounded but flat 2-seeded pods at the base and tiny white flowers at the tip, is characteristic. In the closely related *L. virginicum* the petals are usually longer than the sepals. The Field Peppergrass (*L. campestre*), with clasping leaves, is most common in vacant lots in and around cities. Peppergrass and dandelions make a delicious salad.

GARLIC MUSTARD
(Alliaria officinalis)

This introduced mustard is becoming a troublesome weed in open woodlands and, especially, in city ravines, where it quickly carpets the ground to the exclusion of the native plants. Also found along roadsides and near dwellings, it flowers in May and June and grows mainly in southern Ontario. The scalloped leaf margins, purple stem bases, 4-petalled flowers, and long, thin, upward-pointing seed pods are diagnostic features to check for. The young leaves can be used as a tangy addition to a salad.

(108)

TOOTHWORT
(Dentaria diphylla)
Crinkleroot, Pepperwort

The raceme of large white 4-petalled flowers makes this plant easy to spot in the moist spring woodlands where it grows. Occurring in colonies and flowering in May, it is typically a plant of the Mixed Forest and often grows along streams or in swampy areas. It has 2 coarsely toothed alternate leaves with 3 broad divisions. The Cut-leaved Toothwort (*D. laciniata*), a more southern species, has a whorl of 3 deeply cut compound leaves, each with 3 very narrow divisions. Hybrids occur where these two mustards are found together. The pungent peppery odour of the rhizomes is characteristic of the Mustard family.

SHEPHERD'S PURSE
(Capsella bursa-pastoris)

Look under almost any fence in the city, or check the edge of almost any lawn, and this tiny Mustard is sure to be there. Present throughout Ontario as an annual or winter annual, it not only abounds in the urban setting but flourishes in many grain fields. A Eurasian species, its most distinctive feature is its heart-shaped seed pods, from which it gets its name. The stem and leaves are usually covered with fine hairs, and the bases of the leaves clasp the stem. Flowering continues from early spring to late fall.

DAME'S ROCKET
(Hesperis matronalis)

Brought to North America by the settlers as a decorative garden plant, this tall perennial has escaped cultivation and become naturalized. It often flourishes in large colonies around old homesteads or in moist shady places near streams. In May and June the colourful masses of white, pink, or purple flowers can easily be found along roadsides in southern Ontario. Note the sandpaper texture of the large toothed leaves. The typical 4 petals in the form of a cross and the long slender fruits indicate a member of the Mustard family.

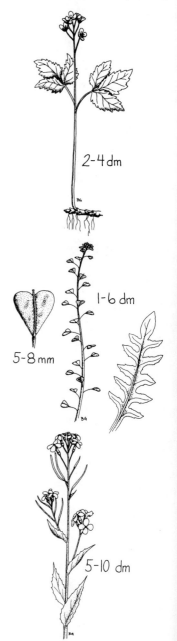

2-4 dm

1-6 dm

5-8 mm

5-10 dm

(109)

7-35 cm

ROUND-LEAVED SUNDEW
(*Drosera rotundifolia*)

This tiny tentacled plant must supplement its nitrogen uptake in its nutrient-poor environment by "feeding" on insects. Growing in moist acid sand or moss, it is often difficult to find until the sun reflects the glitter of the sticky dewdrops at the tip of the reddish hairs which cover the leaves. Insects attracted to the sweet glistening secretion become entangled by the stickiness, and later the all-important nitrogen, as well as other nutrients, are absorbed by the plant. This is the commonest and most widespread Sundew in Ontario. The Linear-leaved Sundew (*D. linearis*) may be seen in the wet sands on the west side of the Bruce Peninsula, while the Intermediate Sundew (*D. intermedia*), with small spoon-shaped leaves occurs on muddy lake margins in the Canadian Shield area.

TO 4 dm

EARLY SAXIFRAGE
(*Saxifraga virginiensis*)

The broadly toothed oval leaves form a rosette at the base of the plant from which a thick fleshy and hairy stalk arises to support the flowers. At first the inflorescence is very compact, but later it becomes more open. Growing in rocky exposed situations, this plant flowers from the end of April to mid-May, and by June or July it is difficult to see any signs of its former presence. The genus name *Saxifraga* means "to break rocks".

1-3.5 dm

FOAMFLOWER
(*Tiarella cordifolia*)

The fluffy mass of white flowers with long protruding stamens and narrow petals must have reminded someone of a soapy foam. Flowering in rich damp woods in May and June throughout the Mixed Forest region, it prefers low-lying wet cedar woods. Although the leaves are similar to those of Mitrewort they differ in being larger, and there are no stem-leaves on the flowering stalk. Each flower produces 2 fruits, but one is larger than the other, resulting in the lopsided appearance.

MITREWORT
(Mitella diphylla)

The petal blades are so deeply divided that each of the tiny flowers on the spike-like inflorescence looks like a snowflake crystal. Although the basal leaves look similar to those of the Foamflower, the 2 smaller sessile leaves attached below the flowers are distinctive. Search for this plant in rich woods in May and early June. When the fruit, for which the plant receives its name, breaks open, it shows the shiny black seeds inside. Further north and in cooler bogs in the south, the Naked Mitrewort (M. nuda) has either 1 or sometimes no stem-leaf below its yellowish-green flowers, and its leaves appear more rounded.

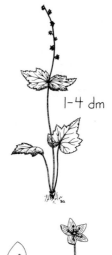

1-4 dm

GRASS OF PARNASSUS
(Parnassia glauca)

You will find this attractive plant blooming in late summer in moist shoreline meadows around the Great Lakes, especially on the west shore of the Bruce Peninsula. The solitary flowers are held high above the basal rosette of smooth either spade-like or heart-shaped leaves. The white petals are etched with greenish veins. Although there are 5 typical stamens, others have been modified, probably to attract insect pollinators. This, our most common *Parnassia* sp., has 3-parted sterile stamens which are a little shorter than the fertile ones.

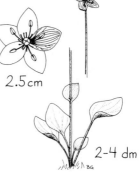

2.5 cm

2-4 dm

COMMON STRAWBERRY
(Fragaria virginiana)

Not too many people need an introduction to this wild plant with its runners and tasty fruits, since it looks so similar to the domestic variety. There are two wild strawberry species in Ontario. The common native plant, which frequents fields and open places, has blunt-tipped leaflets, and its small "seeds" are embedded in pits in the roundish fruit; while the Wood Strawberry (F. vesca) has more pointed leaflets, and the fruit surface appears bumpy because its "seeds" are not in pits. F. vesca also differs in that its flowers and fruits extend above the leaves, and it matures a little later.

6-15 cm

1-3m

WHITE SWEET CLOVER
(Melilotus alba)

Flowering from midsummer to autumn, this European introduction has been used as a forage crop and is a very important source of nectar for honey-producing bees. In addition, like the other clovers, it has the ability to improve the nitrogen content of the soil in which it grows. Often assuming a bushy appearance, this fragrant species rapidly establishes itself on waste ground along roadways and field edges. It differs from the true clovers in having stalked leaflets, and in having its boat-shaped flowers on a slender elongated stalk rather than condensed into a stout head.

6-15cm

WHITE CLOVER
(Trifolium repens)

Check for the pale inverted V on each of the 3 roundish leaflets of this low creeping clover, which frequents roadsides and fields. The small pea-like flowers are in globular heads which are held above the leaves on separate stems. The flowers turn brown with age. Introduced from Europe, this clover is used as forage, but it also grows in lawns. At night, the leaflets fold back along their midribs. This action is referred to as a "sleeping response", and is perhaps a means of conserving water.

2-4 dm

CANADA VIOLET
(Viola canadensis)

This delicate, stemmed violet of rich Mixed and Deciduous woods has downy purplish stems and heart-shaped leaves. You will notice that the petals are white with dark veins (nectar guides), which point to the yellow petal bases and to the spur containing the nectar. Each petal is tinged with bluish purple on the back. Flowering usually occurs in May. The Northern White Violet (V. pallens) grows in low wet woods. Referred to as a stemless violet, its smaller flowers and smooth basal leaves are on separate stalks. In drier woods, the Sweet White Violet (V. blanda), also stemless, has twisted upper petals, a reddish stem, and hairy upper leaf surfaces. Both these violets are fragrant.

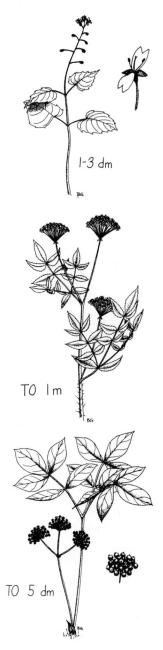

NORTHERN ENCHANTER'S NIGHTSHADE
(Circaea alpina)

Growing in moist cool woodlands throughout most of Ontario, this low perennial blooms from July to September. It has a succulent pale-green appearance and opposite heart-shaped smooth leaves. The fruits are covered with bristly hooked hairs, which easily attach themselves to animals' fur and to the hiker's sock, offering an efficient means of dispersing the seeds to new areas. The more southerly Enchanter's Nightshade (*C. quadrisulcata*) is darker green and less coarsely toothed, but larger in all respects. It rarely extends into the Canadian Shield region.

1-3 dm

BRISTLY SARSAPARILLA
(Aralia hispida)

Look for the roundish white flower clusters of this tall member of the Ginseng family in June and July. It occurs in open dry (often sandy) woods, especially in the region of the Canadian Shield, but less commonly north and south of it. The doubly compound leaves and a stem which is bristly at the base but smooth higher up, are distinctive features. Later in the summer, dark blue or purple berries, which are eaten by birds and small mammals, replace the flowers in their characteristic umbel arrangement. Members of this family differ from those of the Parsley family in having more than 2 styles and fleshy, rather than dry, fruits.

TO 1 m

WILD SARSAPARILLA
(Aralia nudicaulis)

Unlike its bristly relative above, the leaves and flowers of this plant occur on separate smooth stalks. The single leaf is divided into 3 compound leaflets and is taller than the flowering stalk, which usually bears 3 circular greenish-white umbels. Later, dark-blue berries are produced. Flowering in late May and June in dry or moist open woods, it can be found throughout almost all Ontario. Used in northeastern North America for adding flavour to Root Beer, the aromatic rhizomes are a substitute for the roots of the true Sarsaparilla, a tropical vine.

TO 5 dm

(113)

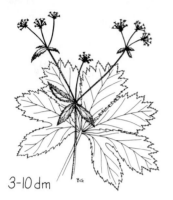

BLACK SNAKEROOT
(Sanicula marilandica)

This member of the Parsley family flowers during late spring and early summer. Look for it in moist woods and edges of swamps in the Mixed Forest region. Several greenish-white flower heads rise above the distinctive, 7-parted palmately compound leaves. Bristly, oval, bur-like fruits appear later, become 5-8 mm long, and are dispersed by adhesion to animals' fur and clothing. Some plants with the common name Snakeroot were used by the Indians as a remedy for snakebite. This plant should not be confused with White Snakeroot (p. 123), which differs in having more compact flowering heads and simple opposite leaves.

3-10 dm

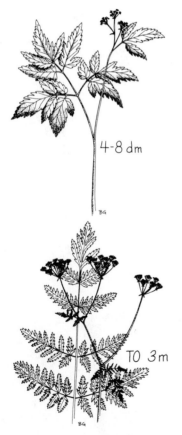

4-8 dm

SWEET CICELY
(Osmorhiza claytoni)

Sweet Cicely blooms in early summer in moist Deciduous and Mixed woodlands. A few scattered umbels stand above the 1 or 2 leaves. Each leaf has 3 leaflets divided into about 5 sub-leaflets. The foliage is softly hairy. The long slender fruits (1 cm) have straight ascending bristles. All members of the *Osmorhiza* genus have scented roots and some have edible roots, but those of this species, the most common in our area, are not at all tasty.

POISON HEMLOCK
(Conium maculatum)

Like so many members of the Parsley family, this plant has a compound umbel type of inflorescence. A tall Eurasian biennial with hollow stems spotted with purple, it is notoriously poisonous and should never be eaten. The finely divided compound leaves may be up to 30 cm long. Found in southern Ontario in wet open sites and waste places, it blooms from June to September. It is believed that Socrates, the great Greek philosopher, died from drinking the juice of this plant. Care should be taken not to identify this poisonous plant incorrectly as Queen Anne's Lace, whose stem is always hairy.

TO 3m

(114)

WATER HEMLOCK
(*Cicuta maculata*)

This highly poisonous native plant of marshlands, swamps, and thickets occurs throughout Ontario. Blooming from June to August, its flat-topped inflorescences are 5-12 cm across. Broad flat fruits, 2-4 mm long, with thick vertical ribs, develop on the bractless umbels. Each leaf is 2 or 3 times compound, with a thin inflated petiole joining the leaf to the purple-streaked stem. Note that the veins lead to the notches between the teeth. Care should be taken not to confuse this plant with edible members of the Parsley family. Bulb-bearing Water Hemlock (*C. bulbifera*), has linear sub-leaflets, and bulblets which give rise to new plants.

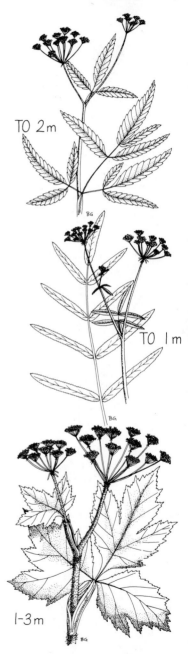

WATER PARSNIP
(*Sium suave*)

This plant of swampy or muddy meadows and shores often has two types of leaves. Out of the water, the compound leaves have 7-17 linear leaflets with sharp teeth, but the submerged leaves are usually very finely divided and look more like a parsley leaf. Check for the broad petiole bases. Each inflorescence has 5-8 bractlets beneath it. Water Parsnip is found throughout the province, and blooms from July to August.

COW PARSNIP
(*Heracleum lanatum*)

Although perennial from an underground root, this plant grows relatively tall in the short space of a summer and is one of our largest native herbs. Watch for it in moist places, especially along streams. Its leaves with their broadly inflated petioles are divided into 3 segments, each over 30 cm long, while the hollow red stems often exceed 4 cm in diameter. The semi-circular flower heads can be up to 20 cm across; in early summer the petals of the outer flowers are larger than the others. An introduced Mediterranean species (*H. mantegazzianum*) is even larger, has more dissected leaves, and may cause a serious dermatitis upon contact with the skin.

(115)

QUEEN ANNE'S LACE
(Daucus carota)
Wild Carrot

The delicate pattern of each flat-topped inflorescence is very much like that of fine lace-work. Distinctive 3-pronged bracts occur beneath the main flower cluster. This introduced biennial blooms from early summer to autumn. Characteristic of roadsides, vacant lots, and fields, it occurs throughout most of Ontario. After flowering, the outer umbels curl in to form a cup-like structure which persists through the winter. The bristly fruits are distributed either by adhering to animals and clothing, or by tumbling across snow-covered fields, carried by strong winter winds. The feathery leaves and pungent smell are similar to those of cultivated carrot.

SHINLEAF
(Pyrola elliptica)

The evergreen basal leaves and the nodding creamy-white flowers with long decurved styles are characteristic. The petals are green veined, and the thin rectangular leaf blades are longer than their petioles. This, our most common species of *Pyrola*, occurs over much of Ontario in dry or moist woods. Also blooming from June to August, Pink Pyrola (*P. asarifolia*) has pink flowers and roundish darker green and thick leaves. The smaller One-sided Pyrola (*Orthilia secunda*) has its greenish-white flowers only on one side of the flower stalk.

ONE-FLOWERED WINTERGREEN
(Moneses uniflora)

The generic name, *Moneses*, can be translated from the Greek as "one delight", which is an excellent name for this tiny inhabitant of moist cool woods or bogs of the Boreal and Mixed Forest regions. During July and August, the solitary fragrant flower, with its waxy white or pink-tinged petals, nods shyly toward the ground. The 3 or 4 roundish evergreen leaves frequently are nestled in a carpet of moss. Note the distinctive 5-parted stigma.

PIPSISSEWA
(Chimaphila umbellata)

The genus name *Chimaphila* means "winter lover" and refers to the evergreen nature of the thick shiny leaves (3-7 cm). The white to pale-pink flower (1-1.5 cm across) has 10 stamens, each with 2 terminal pores which may help to distribute small amounts of pollen to successive pollinators. Flowers appear from June to August. Capsules are 5-6 mm across. Pipsissewa occurs throughout much of Ontario, but is most abundant in the Canadian Shield region, often in the acid soil of Oak-Pine woods.

BASTARD TOADFLAX
(Comandra umbellata)

Found on dry slopes, in dry open woods, on prairies, and on limestone barrens throughout much of Ontario, this interesting plant is a member of the Sandalwood family, chiefly a tropical group. It is reported to be a root parasite like Painted Cup (p. 149) and Beech-drops (p. 187). Leaves are very narrow in some populations (8 times as long as wide) but very wide in other populations (barely 3 times as long as wide). The flowers, produced in May and June, range from 3 to 5 mm long. The fruit is a dry nut 4-6 mm in diameter. Variety *decumbens* (previously *C. richardsiana*) is distinguished by its shorter, more or less flat-topped, inflorescence.

WOOD-SORREL
(Oxalis montana)

The attractive flowers (2-2.5 cm across) are white or pinkish with purple or reddish veining. The flowering season is rather short, extending from late June to early July, but non-opening inconspicuous flowers are produced later in the season on recurved stalks. The leaves have a sour taste as do those of Sheep-sorrel (p. 150), but the two are not closely related. Wood-sorrel occurs in rich woods and on mossy hummocks in coniferous swamps in the Boreal and Mixed Forest regions. The evidence suggests that the Irish Shamrock is the same as the European Wood-sorrel (*O. acetosella*), a species very similar to ours. (See also introduced sorrels, p. 136.)

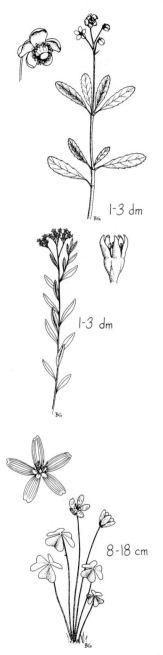

1-3 dm

1-3 dm

8-18 cm

(117)

BUNCHBERRY
(Cornus canadensis)

Most frequent in the Canadian Shield region and the north, this plant grows in colonies in moist woodlands, often in openings or along paths. The 4 large "petals" are actually bracts, and the "inner flower parts" are a whole inflorescence of greenish-white flowers which later matures into a cluster of attractive bright-red berries. Pairs of opposite leaves, set close together on the stem, produce the characteristic false whorl of 4-6 leaves. The vein pattern is typical of the dogwoods, and Bunchberry is the only non-woody member of the family in Ontario. Birds like to eat the fruits.

WINTERGREEN
(Gaultheria procumbens)

In July and August, this aromatic plant produces small urn-shaped waxy flowers that hang from the axils of the leaves. The creeping stem can often be seen running along the ground or just beneath the surface of the moss carpet. The leaves are evergreen, and the red "berries" also remain over winter. The fruits are capsules which have been covered by a fleshy calyx, resulting in their berry-like appearance. The familiar wintergreen flavour is present in fresh foliage and fruits. Wintergreen is found in cool, either dry or boggy, woods and clearings throughout much of Ontario except the extreme southwest.

STAR-FLOWER
(Trientalis borealis)

Usually 7 petals form the points of the delicate star-like flowers which appear in late May and June on thin stalks above the shiny leaves. This low smooth perennial of moist woodlands is easily recognized by its whorl of 5-9 slender leaves at the top of the stem. When flowers are absent there is the possibility of confusing this plant with Indian Cucumber-root (p. 128), which has leaves with a number of parallel veins rather than one mid-vein. Star-flower occurs in the Boreal and Mixed forests, but only in cooler sites southward.

BUCKBEAN
(Menyanthes trifoliata)

Its thick fleshy leaves emerge from the shallow water at the edge of a pond, marsh or bog. The botanical name *trifoliata* refers to the 3 leaflets, a characteristic shared with various members of the Pea or Bean family. When Buckbean flowers in late May and June, each petal is covered on its inner surface with a fringe of fine hairs. More common in the north, it is less frequent south of the Canadian Shield region. It is interesting that there are 2 kinds of flowers: those with styles much longer than the stamens, and others with the style shorter than the stamens.

FIELD BINDWEED
(Convolvulus arvensis)

Small (less than 2.5 cm), white or pinkish funnel-shaped flowers come from the axils of the arrow-shaped leaves of this European introduction. Found along roadsides, in waste places, or in fields, Field Bindweed flowers continuously after early summer. Sometimes it becomes a serious weed as it trails or climbs on vegetation, often forming dense tangled mats. Although more common in the south, it occurs as far north as the L. Superior region. A native member of the Morning Glory family, the Hedge Bindweed (*C. sepium*), has larger, usually pink, flowers (to 5 cm) and larger leaves with blunt rather than pointed basal lobes.

VIRGINIA WATERLEAF
(Hydrophyllum virginianum)

In damp shady woods or along stream banks, these bell-like flowers with protruding stamens hang in drooping white or violet clusters during May and June. The leaves are pinnately divided, with pale "water markings" on the upper surface; the inflorescence, at first coiled, rises above them. The Broad-leaved Waterleaf (*H. canadense*) is larger, has hairy simple leaves that are lobed like those of a maple, and the flower cluster is never as high as the uppermost leaf. Both species are found in southern Ontario, mostly outside the Canadian Shield region.

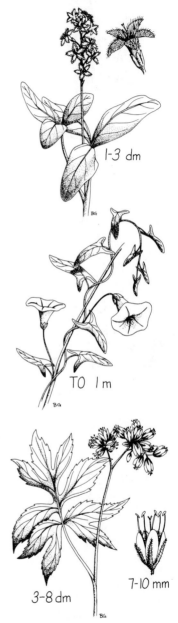

1-3 dm

TO 1 m

7-10 mm

3-8 dm

4-15dm

TO 1.5 m

3-5 cm

2-8 dm

WHITE VERVAIN
(*Verbena urticifolia*)

Only a few of the many tiny flowers are ever open at the same time on the long narrow spike. Although similar in general appearance to the Stinging Nettles, the leaves and stem are without any stinging hairs. A blotchy mildew is often present on the leaves and is characteristic of this species. Found mainly south of the Canadian Shield region, White Vervain prefers rich thickets and borders of woods, but also grows in moist fields and waste places. The tiny nutlet fruits are sometimes eaten by birds.

THORN APPLE
(*Datura stramonium*)

A very poisonous plant, this introduced annual occurs in fields and waste places. Its large, showy, funnel-shaped flowers (to 10 cm), which hang from the leaf axils, made it a popular garden plant and account for the common name of "Angel's-trumpet". The blossoms, appearing in summer and autumn, are followed by a 4-valved spiny seed pod, an attractive but dangerous plaything. This plant is one of the chief causes of plant poisonings in children. An unpleasant smell also characterizes this species.

CUT-LEAVED
WATER-HOREHOUND
(*Lycopus americanus*)

The square stem, opposite leaves, and 2-lipped flowers distinguish this plant as a mint even though it is not fragrant. From late June to September it may be found in marshes and low woods or along wet shores north to the Boreal Forest. Tiny white flowers with petals hardly longer than the sepals occur in tight clusters in the leaf axils. The deeply cut, almost lobed, leaves and the long narrow calyx lobes distinguish this common species from *L. uniflorus*, which has triangular calyx lobes that are much shorter than its flaring petals. The introduced *L. europaeus* has broader, prominently veined leaves, with stiff hairs on the upper surface.

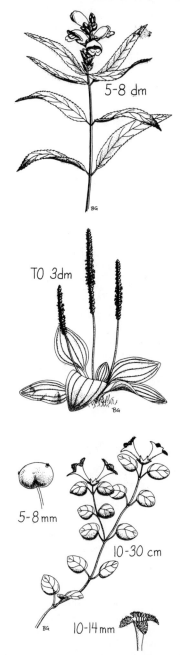

TURTLEHEAD
(Chelone glabra)

In swamps, wet woods, or thickets, along streams and in ditches, the large creamy white flowers appear in mid to late summer. With a little imagination, each flower becomes a turtle's head which has its mouth slightly open. Narrowly toothed opposite leaves are borne on tall smooth stems. Although widespread in Ontario, Turtlehead is locally rare; for example, in the southern parts of the Shield region. Flowering occurs in late summer. Although it might be confused with a mint, it has roundish, rather than square stems, and actually belongs to the Snapdragon family.

COMMON PLANTAIN
(Plantago major)

Roadsides, lawns, and waste places throughout Ontario harbour this introduced plant which flowers from early summer well into the autumn. The almost parallel-veined basal leaves and elongated but compact flowering spike are key identification features. The roundish fruits have "lids" which come off and allow the small seeds to be dispersed. Pale Plantain (*P. rugelii*) has purplish rather than green petioles, and more slender spikes than the common species; the slender fruits have "lids" that detach below the middle, rather than at the middle. The Ribgrass (*P. lanceolata*) has pale, 3-veined, grass-like leaves and a relatively short dense spike on a tall stem.

PARTRIDGEBERRY
(Mitchella repens)

Dark evergreen leaves set opposite one another on a trailing stem, and the whitened mid-vein along each one, serve to identify this creeping woodland herb at any time of year. The fragrant funnel-shaped flowers, each with 4 bearded lobes, may be tinged with pink, but always occur at the ends of branches, and always in pairs, their ovaries united. Red berry-like fruits with a dark "eye" on each half remain on the plant all winter. Characteristic of the Mixed Forest region, this plant is rather local elsewhere.

(121)

3-10dm

TO 3 m

4-15 dm

NORTHERN BEDSTRAW
(Galium boreale)

The whorls of 4 smooth 3-veined leaves, and tiny flowers in clusters at the tips of branches, distinguish this plant. The square stems are smooth and the plant has an erect habit. It flowers from late spring to late summer. The fruits look like 2 small spheres set side by side. Look for this bedstraw along shores and gravelly or rocky banks in the Boreal and Mixed Forest regions. With inflorescences of 3 flowers held on stalks at the nodes, Fragrant Bedstraw (G. triflorum) has whorls of 6 leaves and smooth stems, while Cleavers (G. aparine) has whorls of 8 leaves and a rough stem. Both these species have weak reclining stems and bristly fruits. They prefer woodlands.

POKEWEED
(Phytolacca americana)

Only rarely found beyond the Carolinian zone, Pokeweed grows along roadsides, in clearings, and in woodlands. The upright racemes of greenish-white flowers are often borne opposite the leaves. The flowers have 5 petal-like sepals, the stems are smooth and reddish. In autumn, the shiny blackish-purple berries hanging on bright-reddish stalks are very attractive. During the spring the young unfolded leaves of Pokeweed were collected by Indians and prepared as a vegetable. The rest of the plant is poisonous, including the mature leaves. A crimson dye can be prepared from the berries.

BONESET
(Eupatorium perfoliatum)

Flowering in late summer and fall, Boneset inhabits swamps, river banks, damp thickets, and even ditches in the Boreal and Mixed Forest regions. Each pair of dull green hairy and coarsely veined leaves are united to one another around the stem. During the Middle Ages, this member of the Aster family was prescribed for people with broken bones, since it was hoped that their bones would heal and grow together, just as the leaves of this plant were so successfully joined.

WHITE SNAKEROOT
(Eupatorium rugosum)

White Snakeroot prefers alkaline soils in rich woods and thickets and occurs mainly to the south of the Canadian Shield. The stem and the heart-shaped opposite leaves are smooth. Blooming from July to September, it has flat-topped clusters of white flower heads originating in the axils of the upper leaves. This plant differs from other members of the Aster family in having only disc flowers. White Snakeroot is poisonous to cattle, and the poison can be transmitted to human beings through the tainted milk.

3-15 dm

SILVER-ROD
(Solidago bicolor)

This is our only white "goldenrod". From a tuft of large, long-stalked, basal leaves at the ground level, the leaves become progressively smaller higher up the stem. The inflorescence is wand-like with a thick cylinder of flowers at the top of the hairy stem. A native member of the Aster family, Silver-rod grows in dry open woods and on rocky outcrops in southern Ontario and seems to prefer acid soils. The Hairy Goldenrod (*S. hispida*), which differs mainly in having yellow rays, appears to favour less acid soils and extends north to the Boreal Forest although it is also common in the south. Both species flower in late August and September.

1-12 dm

HEATH ASTER
(Aster ericoides)

A delicate feathery appearance draws attention to this common autumn wildflower of abandoned fields and dry open places. It has many stiff narrow grey-hairy leaves resembling the leaves of some shrubs in the Heath family. Many small white-rayed flowering heads are densely crowded on 1-sided racemes. The purple-flowered New England Aster blooms with the Heath Aster, and an attractive hybrid called the Amethyst Aster (*A.* × *amethystinus*) is sometimes produced. This has pale-blue rays and narrow leaves. Heath Aster is common in southern Ontario but becomes less frequent farther north in the Mixed Forest region.

3-10 dm

3-12 dm

3-20 dm

1-15 dm

CALICO ASTER
(Aster lateriflorus)

Purplish disc florets surrounded by white ray florets help to distinguish this fall-flowering aster. Common along roadsides, in open woodlands, and along shores, it occurs north to the Boreal Forest. Each of the side branches with their 1-sided racemes is held at right angles to the main stem and is supported by a stalkless toothed leaf. Leaves in the inflorescence are large and sparse instead of numerous and small as in the Heath Aster (p. 123). The bracts around the flowering heads have green midribs and tips.

FLAT-TOPPED WHITE ASTER
(Aster umbellatus)

With wider "petals" (in ray florets) and a distinctive flat-topped inflorescence, this large smooth aster grows in moist areas such as low thickets, meadows, and ditches. It can often be seen flowering with Joe-Pye-weed and Boneset during August and September. Found throughout the province except in the Tundra zone, it is most frequent in the Mixed Forest region. The tips of the lance-shaped leaves are drawn out into long points, and although they do not have toothed margins they are extremely rough-edged with fine bristly hairs. The pappus hairs on top of the seeds are two different lengths — a good distinguishing feature.

HORSEWEED
(Conyza canadensis)

This native member of the Aster family might readily fall into the category of a troublesome weed of waste places, roadsides, and cultivated fields. It has inconspicuous flowers with white or sometimes pinkish rays, and is much more noticeable when in fruit with the white pappus showing than when it is in full flower. The numerous linear leaves and many small flower heads in the leaf axils are characteristic features. Flowering occurs from July to October. Horseweed plants may be 5 cm high with 5 flower heads or 2 m high with several hundred flowering heads, depending on local environmental conditions.

FIELD PUSSY-TOES
(Antennaria neglecta)

A soft covering of white woolly hairs over the flower buds is a characteristic feature of this plant. Found in dry fields, pastures, or open woods, it is most common in the Mixed Forest region. Flowering occurs in April and May. The basal leaves are generally smooth on the top and densely woolly beneath. The 3-5 parallel veins of the Plantain-leaved Pussy-toes (*A. plantaginifolia*) distinguishes it from the Field Pussy-toes which has smaller leaves with a single vein. Both species of Pussy-toes have a basal rosette of leaves unlike the similar Pearly Everlasting.

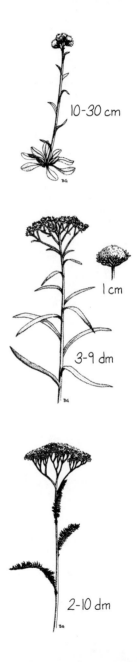

10-30 cm

PEARLY EVERLASTING
(Anaphalis margaritacea)

This member of the Aster family is named for the dry paper-thin bracts which surround each flower head. These persist well into the autumn and winter after the individual florets are lost, making the plant ideal for dry bouquets. The pearly white inflorescence, appearing in summer, is almost flat-topped and is made up entirely of "disc" florets with the male and female flowers borne on different plants. A cottony down covers the stems as well as the under surface of the long slender leaves. Found throughout much of the province, it prefers dry open rocky or sandy situations.

1 cm

3-9 dm

YARROW
(Achillea millefolium)

Introduced from Europe, Yarrow is a common plant of meadows, roadsides, and waste ground, and can be found almost anywhere in Ontario. Each leaf, 3-15 cm long, is divided many times to appear fine and feathery as if it were composed of a thousand parts. The many small heads in a flat-topped inflorescence each have about 5 ray florets. Flowering occurs throughout the summer and into autumn. The genus name *Achillea* refers to the Greek hero Achilles, who is reported to have used the crushed leaves to stop the bleeding of his soldiers' wounds. The sap apparently acts as a coagulant.

2-10 dm

(125)

1-6 dm

2-8 dm

11-14 mm

4-15 dm

MAYWEED
(Anthemis cotula)

Mayweed is sometimes confused with the Ox-eye Daisy, but differs in having finely dissected leaves, a strong disagreeable odour, and a bitter taste. Dogs and farmyard animals usually avoid it. It has relatively small flowering heads with drooping rather than spreading ray flowers (each 6-10 mm long), and the yellow centre of disc flowers is dome-shaped. It often forms colonies along roadsides and in waste places. An introduced species, it blooms from June to October but not in May as its name might suggest.

OX-EYE DAISY
(Chrysanthemum leucanthemum)

Found throughout most of Ontario, the large bright "flowers" (4-6 cm across) appear from June to August. The yellow "eye" of the solitary "flower" is depressed in the centre and is made up of many tightly packed disc flowers, surrounded by larger white ray flowers. The dark-green leaves are variously lobed and cut. Imported from Europe by early settlers for their gardens, Ox-eye Daisy is sometimes common in pasture lands and is frequent along roadsides. A medicinal tea can be prepared from this plant.

WHITE LETTUCE
(Prenanthes alba)

Drooping clusters of bell-like flower heads occur at the top of tall leafy stems in late summer and autumn. The 8-12 protruding ray flowers are white, but the pappus is cinnamon brown. Leaves decrease in size from the base to the top of the smooth purplish stem, which is covered with a whitish bloom. Preferring rich woods and thickets, it occurs mainly in the Mixed Forest zone and less commonly elsewhere in the province. Tall White Lettuce (P. altissima) grows in moist woods in southern Ontario. It has a creamy white pappus and the 5-6 rays in each head are greenish-white. A sticky white sap is characteristic of both species. (See also Lactuca, p. 171.)

LARGE-FLOWERED BELLWORT
(Uvularia grandiflora)

During the late spring, pale yellow bell-like flowers (2.5-5 cm long) are suspended gracefully from drooping stems. Produced from an underground rhizome, the stem is generally forked. Clasping the stem are pale-green leaves whose lobes project on each side of it. Downy white hairs cover their under surfaces. This plant is found in rich woods of the Deciduous and Mixed Forest. Sessile Bellwort or Wild Oats (*U. sessilifolia*) has smaller pale yellow to cream flowers; and its leaves, which are whitish and smooth beneath, are sessile but do not surround the stem. Although less common, it too is absent from the Canadian Shield region.

2-10dm

TROUT LILY
(Erythronium americanum)
Yellow Adder's Tongue, Dog-Tooth Violet

In early spring most of our Deciduous and Mixed Forest woodlands have extensive patches of bright-yellow flowers scattered amidst many small tongue-shaped leaves with "speckled trout" mottling. A nodding flower is produced between each pair of leaves, but colonies have many solitary leaves without flowers. The White Trout Lily (*E. albidum*), mainly confined to the Carolinian zone, occurs on wooded river-valley slopes. Its flowers are pale cream while the leaves are bluish-green with little to no brown mottling.

1-2 dm

BLUEBEAD-LILY
(Clintonia borealis)

During late May and June, several (2-8) yellowish-green bell-like flowers, in a loose umbel, open at the top of the leafless flowering stalk. By late summer, deep blue berries have formed on short ascending pedicels. The 2-4 broad basal leaves look similar to those of the Pink Lady's-slipper, except that they are smooth and shiny. This lily grows in cool moist woodlands, mostly in the Mixed and Boreal Forest regions, sparingly elsewhere in the province.

1.5-4 dm

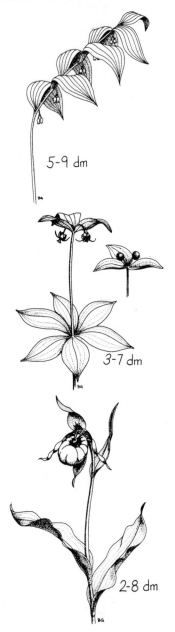

5-9 dm

3-7 dm

2-8 dm

SOLOMON'S SEAL
(Polygonatum pubescens)

In May and June, greenish-yellow tubular flowers (7-13 mm) dangle in pairs on forked stalks from the leaf axils. By midsummer, they have been replaced by bluish-black berries. The leaves, which look similar to those of the False Solomon's Seal, are more or less stalkless, with soft hairs along the veins of the under surface. This lily of rich woodlands is most common in the Mixed Forest zone. Both the generic and common names refer to the many joints (scars from prior stalks) on the underground rhizome which, when broken, looks like a wax seal.

INDIAN CUCUMBER-ROOT
(Medeola virginiana)

The whorl of 5-9 leaves is suggestive of a Star Flower, but in flowering specimens, the second whorl of 3-4 smaller broader leaves supports hanging greenish-yellow, 6-parted flowers. Flowering occurs from late May to July. Late in the summer, purple berries are held above the upper whorl of leaves. Indian Cucumber-root is commonly found in the moist acid woods of the southern Canadian Shield region and locally elsewhere in southern Ontario.

YELLOW LADY'S SLIPPER
(Cypripedium calceolus)

The shiny bright-yellow "slipper" (the lip) of this orchid is really a modified petal. Pollinating bees enter through the large opening in the top, but because of the incurved margins and smooth inner edges, they are forced to leave by one of two smaller openings near the base of the flower — first passing the stigma and depositing any pollen they are carrying, then passing the anther and picking up a new pollen load. The small variety (var. *parviflorum*) has deep purplish brown, strongly twisted lateral petals 3.5-5 cm long. It prefers tamarack or cedar bogs, or open wet meadows. The large variety (var. *pubescens*) has less twisted greenish-brown lateral petals, 5-9 cm long. It grows in rocky woodlands, bogs, and along lakeshores, but thrives in limestone areas.

(128)

PURSLANE
(Portulaca oleracea)

Thick fleshy foliage and red stems are characteristic features. The small, stalkless, pale-yellow flowers open throughout the summer but only on sunny mornings. Circular fruits with round lids contain tiny black seeds. Producing creeping mats from a thick central root, Purslane frequently extends onto sidewalks or over curbs. It thrives in harsh disturbed environments created by man and has followed him over most of the earth. Watery rather than milky juices are produced, distinguishing it from some of the spurges which it resembles in habit. This plant may be used in salads and cooked as a vegetable.

SPATTERDOCK
(Nuphar variegatum)

This aquatic is found throughout Ontario in ponds, bays, and slow-moving streams. It blooms during the summer. The bright-yellow flowers (about 5 cm across) protrude several centimetres above the water on thick stalks. Heart-shaped floating leaves may be up to 20 cm broad and always have rounded lobes. Spatterdock is an important part of the aquatic environment. It greatly increases the surface area and complexity of the habitat, providing various micro-habitats and cover for numerous aquatic organisms. The foliage also provides food for a variety of animals ranging from moose to insects.

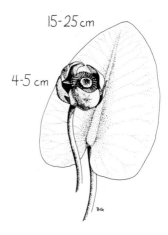

15-25 cm

4-5 cm

MARSH MARIGOLD
(Caltha palustris)

From late April to June these robust plants may be found blooming in wet meadows and swamplands throughout most of Ontario. They add a cheerful colour to the otherwise sombre hues of their early spring surroundings. The blossoms resemble those of many buttercups, but are a good deal larger (up to 4 cm). The bright-yellow petal-like structures are sepals: petals are absent in this species. The roundish to kidney-shaped leaves are shiny, deep green, thick, and fleshy, and the stem is hollow. A clumped or bushy appearance is characteristic.

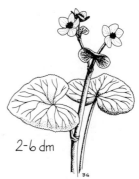

2-6 dm

2-5 dm

KIDNEYLEAF-BUTTERCUP
(Ranunculus abortivus)

Inconspicuous flowers with tiny petals that are scarcely, if at all, longer than the sepals, are produced by this early spring buttercup. It has 2 types of leaves. Those at the base of the plant are roundish or kidney-shaped with long stalks, but further up the stem the leaves become linear, or variously lobed, or divided, and stalkless. This plant inhabits moist woods and thickets in the Deciduous and Mixed Forest regions.

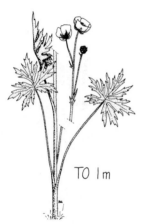

TO Im

TALL BUTTERCUP
(Ranunculus acris)

This European immigrant is our most common summer-flowering buttercup. It not only grows in fields and pastures, where cattle do not eat it because of its bitter taste, but also along roadsides and in waste places throughout most of the province. The petals (to 15 mm) are shiny above and about twice as long as the sepals. The Bristly Buttercup (*R. pensylvanicus*) of moist sites also flowers in summer. Its petals (to 5.5 mm) are shorter than the sepals and its leaves have 3 stalked lobes. Hooked Buttercup (*R. recurvatus*), a woodland species, has pale-yellow petals shorter than its recurved sepals, and leaves that are shallowly 3- or 5-lobed. Swamp Buttercup (*R. septentrionalis*) flowers in late spring. It is found near streams or in moist woods. The petals are longer than the sepals, and each of the 3 stalked leaflets has three lobes.

3-8 dm

CELANDINE
(Chelidonium majus)

Introduced from Eurasia, Celandine occurs in shady moist places especially around cities and towns in southern Ontario. The bright-yellow flowers, 2-2.5 cm across, appear from spring to fall. The 4 broad petals soon fall and a long slender pod (3-5 cm) develops. A member of the poppy family, Celandine produces a clear orange-yellow juice which may cause a dermatitis. The seeds and leaves are poisonous if taken internally.

TUMBLE MUSTARD
(Sisymbrium altissimum)

The introduced Eurasian mustards shown on this page and the next all have flowers with 4 petals in the shape of a cross and long slender fruiting pods. Tumble Mustard has coarsely lobed basal leaves which are hairy, with the terminal lobe no larger than the other lobes. These lower leaves shrivel by flowering time. The upper leaves are smooth, with almost thread-like segments. From June to early autumn, loose clusters of pale-yellow flowers, 6 mm across, form the longest mustard fruits (5-10 cm) of any in Ontario. At maturity the stem breaks at the base and the whole plant is blown by the wind, releasing its seeds along the way. Tumble Mustard occurs in waste ground and fields throughout Ontario.

HEDGE MUSTARD
(Sisymbrium officinale)

Small flowers (3 mm) appear from June to August, followed by upright fruits (1-1.5 cm) that are characteristically held close to the main stem on short stalks (1.5 mm). The basal leaves have definite stalks, and the terminal lobe is rounded and larger than the others. The upper leaves are broader than those of Tumble Mustard. Found throughout southern Ontario and in a few localities in northwestern Ontario, Hedge Mustard usually grows in waste places, in gardens, and at the edges of fields.

WALL ROCKET
(Diplotaxis tenuifolia)

The deeply lobed leaves of Wall Rocket occur mainly at the base of the plant rather than along the stem. From May to September, spreading deep-yellow flowers with petals 10-20 mm give rise to pods 3-5 cm long. An unpleasant odour is produced by this plant, which grows in coarse soils along roads or in waste places in southern Ontario. A smaller Wall Rocket (*D. muralis*) differs in having shorter lemon-yellow petals (5-10 mm) and shorter seeds pods (2-3 cm).

(131)

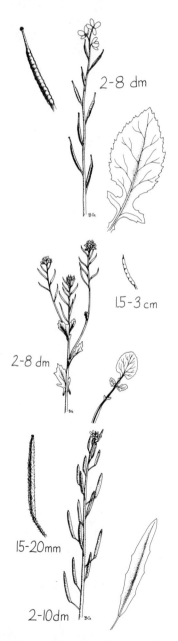

WILD MUSTARD
(Sinapis arvensis)

This common weed of wastelands, roadsides, and cultivated fields occurs throughout most of Ontario. It has large flowers (1.5 cm), short thick fruit stalks (3-5 mm), and ribbed seed pods (3-5 cm) with flattened terminal beaks (up to ½ length of pod). Flowering begins in late May and continues through the summer. Plants are rough-hairy at the base where the leaves are long-stalked. The upper stalkless leaves are coarsely toothed, appearing similar to the terminal lobe of the basal leaves. Indian Mustard (*Brassica juncea*) has few or no hairs, paler yellow flowers, and its slender fruiting stalks are 12 mm long. The taller Black Mustard (*B. nigra*), to 2.5 m, has almost linear upper leaves, and the small seed pods (1-2 cm), with 3 mm seedless beaks, are pressed close to the stem.

WINTER CRESS
(Barbarea vulgaris)

The basal leaves, which last throughout the winter, often have a purplish tinge. Golden-yellow flowers, 1-1.5 cm, are present from mid-May to early July and sometimes reappear late in the autumn. The beaked seed pods, on stalks 3-6 mm, vary from erect and dense to spreading and loosely arranged. Winter Cress occurs throughout most of Ontario in meadows, on wastelands, and along roadsides. Young leaves can be eaten as greens in a salad or cooked as a vegetable.

WORMSEED MUSTARD
(Erysimum cheiranthoides)

Wormseed Mustard has slender leaves with few teeth along the margins. The stem and leaf surfaces are slightly roughened with 2- or 3-branched hairs. Crowded pale-yellow flowers, 6 mm across, appear from mid-June to late fall. The 4-angled seed pods are on stalks 1 cm long. Pigs will refuse to eat their feed if it contains the bitter seeds of this plant. Common throughout Ontario, Wormseed Mustard occurs in fields and along roadsides.

MOSSY STONECROP
(Sedum acre)

This European species has escaped from cultivation. Its horizontal stems and short semi-erect branches often form dense mats covering extensive areas on open dunes or rocks. The pale-green leaves (2-10 mm) are alternate, fleshy, and nearly circular in cross-section. Appearing in June and July, the star-like flowers, 8-10 mm across, vary from bright yellow to yellowish green.

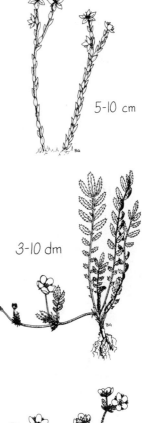

5-10 cm

SILVERWEED
(Potentilla anserina)

The bright-yellow flowers (2-2.5 cm) of Silverweed might be mistaken for those of a Buttercup, but they are solitary on leafless stalks 2-10 cm long, and their petals are not shiny. Rooting occurs at nodes of the slender reddish runners, which trail over the ground much like a Strawberry. The leaves, which are dark green above and silvery silky beneath, have 7-25 toothed segments. Often the leaf rachis is pink or red, and the leaves may lie flat or ascend in tufts. Flowering continues from June to the autumn. Silverweed is found most often on sandy beaches, along rivers, and in sandy or gravelly waste places.

3-10 dm

ROUGH CINQUEFOIL
(Potentilla norvegica)

Rough Cinquefoil is a hairy erect plant, which in June and July has pale-yellow flowers 6-10 mm across in dense leafy clusters. The petals are almost as long as the sepals, which enlarge by fruiting time to cover the seeds. The leaves, each with 3 leaflets, are green on both sides, and have a pair of stipules. Young plants can be distinguished from Strawberries because their leaflets are coarsely toothed right to the base instead of 2/3-3/4 of the way to the base. Able to colonize a wide variety of sites, Rough Cinquefoil is most frequent along roadsides and in pastures or waste places, and occurs throughout Ontario. Sulphur Cinquefoil (*P. recta*), an introduced species, differs in being a perennial with 5-7 palmate leaflets and deep-yellow flowers 2-2.5 cm across.

3-10 dm

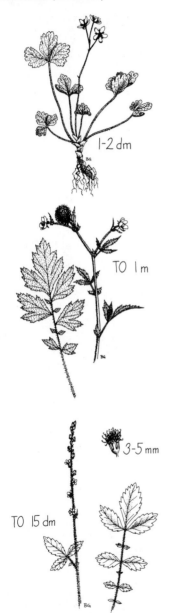

BARREN STRAWBERRY
(Waldsteinia fragarioides)

This plant resembles a Strawberry (*Fragaria* spp.) except that its petals are yellow, it lacks runners, and it does not produce Strawberry-like fruit (hence "Barren"). The leaflets as well as the separate leaf and flower stalks vary from almost smooth to very hairy. In May and June, several flowers occur on stalks about as high as the leaves. The petals are 5-10 mm long. Dry follicle fruits (2-6) are produced later in the summer. Barren Strawberry occurs in moist or dry, often rocky, woods in the Mixed Forest and parts of the Carolinian zone.

YELLOW AVENS
(Geum aleppicum var. *strictum)*

Yellow Avens is a hairy plant with variable leaves; those at the base of the plant are long stalked and pinnately divided, but toward the top the leaves become stalkless with fewer divisions. From early June to late summer, deep yellow to orange 5-parted flowers, 1-2 cm across, occur in wide branching clusters. The hooked fruits which develop into brown bur-like masses (1.4-2.3 cm) are dispersed by catching onto passing animals. Yellow Avens occurs in open woods, in pastures, and along roadsides from the Carolinian to the Boreal Forest region.

AGRIMONY
(Agrimonia gryposepala)

With leaves similar to those of Yellow Avens, Agrimony differs in that its very small yellow flowers (petals about 3 mm) occur in a terminal spike-like inflorescence. There are only 2 pistils, as compared to many present in an Avens flower. Bristly cup-shaped dry fruits (6-8 mm) have hooked hairs around their edges, and are distributed by becoming attached to passing animals. Glands and scattered long hairs are readily seen on the main stem under a 10X magnifier. This woodland plant flowers in July and August. It is found from the Carolinian zone to the northern Mixed Forest region. A closely related species (*A. striata*) is non-glandular but has very downy stems, and all the bristles on the fruits are ascending instead of hooked.

BLACK MEDICK
(Medicago lupulina)

This introduced European species with downy
stems may lie flat on the ground or stand erect with
a spreading habit. Groups of small pea-like flowers
form dense nearly circular clusters about 1 cm
wide and are held on stalks longer than the leaves.
The coiled black seed pods, 1.5-3 mm, are
covered with raised ridges and may be hairy or
smooth. Flowering continues from early spring to
late fall. Black Medick is commonly found in lawns
or gardens, as well as in waste places, roadsides,
and pastures, throughout Ontario. You almost
certainly have it in your lawn, where it may not
flower but can be distinguished from the clovers by
its stalked middle leaflet.

TO 8dm

YELLOW SWEET CLOVER
(Melilotus officinalis)

Similar to the White Sweet Clover (p. 112) but with
yellow flowers, this species is also introduced from
Europe. Both produce the same sweet odour when
their leaves and stems are crushed. They are
excellent honey producers and have been extensively grown for fodder and to improve soil fertility.
Flowers, 5-6 mm long, are produced from May to
October. The Yellow Sweet Clover seems to begin
flowering a little earlier than the White Sweet Clover
growing nearby. Roundish seedpods, 2.5-3.5 mm,
contain 1-2 seeds. Yellow Sweet Clover is to be
found along roadsides, and in fields and on waste
ground, throughout most of Ontario.

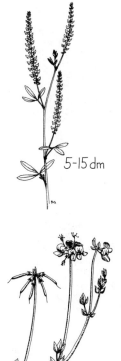

5-15dm

BIRD'S-FOOT TREFOIL
(Lotus corniculatus)

Bright golden-yellow clusters of pea-like flowers
(10-14 mm long) are evident throughout the summer. The plants are often in clumps and may be
erect or lie flat on the ground. As well as 3
clover-like leaflets, each leaf has an extra basal
pair. Brownish to blackish linear pods (2-4 cm)
hang or spread horizontally, giving the impression
of a bird's foot. Cultivated as forage, this European
species often escapes and is becoming more
common along roadsides.

TO 6 dm

(135)

TO 5 dm

YELLOW SORREL
(Oxalis europaea)

The yellow flowers (7-11 mm across) distinguish the sorrels from the clovers, which have similar leaves. Flowering continues from spring to autumn. Borne on spreading or ascending stalks, the capsules (1.5-2.5 cm) explode, ejecting the seeds. The closely related *O. stricta* differs in having its capsule stalks distinctly bent downward. These sorrels grow in dry soil, often along roadsides and in waste places, throughout most of Ontario. The acid leaves can be used sparingly in salads; they are said to be refreshing and to act as a mild tonic. The long-stalked solitary flowers of the Wood Sorrel (p. 117) have notched white petals, 10-15 mm long, with attractive pink veins.

1.5-3 dm

CYPRESS SPURGE
(Euphorbia cyparissias)

This once popular border plant often escapes to roadsides, cemeteries, and fields. The individual flowers are reduced to single stamens and pistils borne in tiny cups. The 3-lobed roundish fruits extend on stalks from the cup. The milky acrid juice produced by the stem and leaves is poisonous, and is a characteristic of the Spurge family to which our Christmas Poinsettia also belongs.

4-8 dm

COMMON ST. JOHN'S-WORT
(Hypericum perforatum)

This European plant was first reported from Pennsylvania in 1793. It rapidly spread throughout North America, and became a serious problem in some areas since it causes sickness in livestock. It was eventually controlled through the introduction of a European beetle that eats the foliage. Hold a leaf up to the light to see small transparent dots scattered over the surface. The attractive flowers (2 cm across) with many bushy stamens, 3 styles, and 5 petals, appear from June to August. It is found throughout much of Ontario in pastures, wastelands, and along roadsides.

DOWNY YELLOW VIOLET
(Viola pubescens)

With downy stems, this yellow Violet is one of the many spring wildflowers that can be found in rich woodlands of the Carolinian and Mixed Forest zones. It is one of the "stemmed" Violets, since its erect stem supports both flowers and leaves. The leaves, 5-12 cm across, have 15-23 teeth on each side. A smooth variety (var. *scabriuscular*) is less downy and has fewer than 15 teeth along the edges of its more slender leaves. Both varieties have purple veins on their yellow petals, and the fruiting capsules may be downy or smooth.

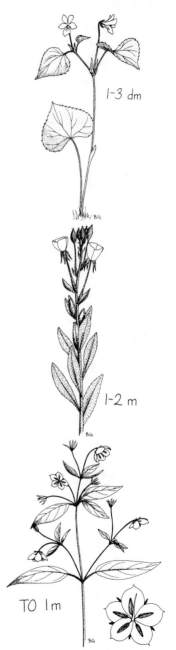

EVENING PRIMROSE
(Oenothera biennis)

By late summer, the tall yellow spikes of Evening Primrose are a common sight along roadsides and in dry open waste places throughout most of Ontario. From July to September, the flowers open in the evening for pollination by bees and moths, but they are short-lived, fading during the following day. Each flower has 4 petals, 4 reflexed sepals, and an X-shaped stigma. A basal rosette produced in the first year is followed by a tall rough-hairy (often reddish) stem with stalkless leaves. Other Evening Primroses differ in flower size, and in the position and shape of the flower parts.

FRINGED LOOSESTRIFE
(Lysimachia ciliata)

Loosestrifes grow in the moist soil of swamps, wet meadows, and marshes, and along shores. They flower from June to August and have opposite leaves. Fringed Loosestrife is distinguished by its fringe of fine hairs along the leaf bases and stalks. Two to four drooping flowers are held on long stalks from the axils of the leaves. Each petal is toothed at the tip. Prairie Loosestrife (*L. quadriflora*) differs in having stiff narrow leaves without fringed margins and in growing mainly near the shores of the Great Lakes. Yellow Loosestrife (*L. terrestris*) is distinct in having dense spikes of star-like flowers, each with a circle or red spots around the centre.

(137)

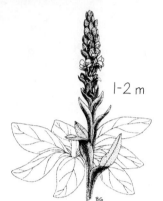

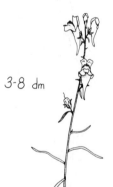

1-2 m

COMMON MULLEIN
(*Verbascum thapsus*)

The remarkable woolly texture and velvety appearance of the leaves of this plant are due to a thick covering of soft branched hairs visible with a 10X magnifier. In the first year of its 2-year cycle, the plant produces a circle of thick yellowish-green leaves lying flat on the ground. In the second year a tall leafy stem is produced, with a densely crowded flowering spike at the top. The 5-lobed flowers, 15-25 mm, appear throughout the summer. Spent brown stalks remain erect for 1 or 2 years and are commonly seen in stony pastures and along roadsides, especially in southern Ontario.

3-8 dm

TOADFLAX
(*Linaria vulgaris*)

Introduced from Europe, Toadflax blooms from June to autumn. Its 5 petals are united to form a pretty 2-lipped flower 2-3 cm long, very similar to a Snapdragon. It is sometimes called Butter and Eggs, because the yellow lower lip has a prominent orange spot as well as a long spur. Egg-shaped seed pods, 9-12 mm, develop after flowering. Dense patches of Toadflax flourish along roadsides and fencerows, and in pastures and waste places, throughout much of Ontario.

1.5-4 dm

WOOD-BETONY
(*Pedicularis canadensis*)

During May and June, the short dense racemes (3-5 cm) of 2-lipped flowers (about 1.5 cm long) vary from completely yellow to completely crimson. The upper lip is narrowly compressed into a hood. Both the upper stem and flower cluster axis are densely hairy. The leaves are so deeply divided that they look like fern fronds. Found in woodlands and clearings in southern Ontario, it occurs only rarely on the Canadian Shield. Swamp-betony (*P. lanceolata*) blooms in late summer, has smooth stems with opposite stalkless leaves, and grows in moist meadows. It, too, occurs in southern Ontario.

GREATER BLADDERWORT
(Utricularia vulgaris)

The finely divided leaves of this small aquatic plant can be seen floating just below the surface of ponds, quiet lakes, and bog pools throughout much of Ontario. Tiny bladders are scattered on the submerged branches and act as traps, in which small aquatic organisms are caught and digested. Blooming occurs from June to August. The flower stalk emerges about 10 cm out of the water, displaying bright-yellow snapdragon-like flowers. Flat-leaved Bladderwort (*U. intermedia*) has bladders on separate branches from its filament-like leaves. Horned Bladderwort (*U. cornuta*), with fine linear leaves and minute bladders, occurs on wet soil.

BLUE-STEMMED GOLDENROD
(Solidago caesia)

Blue-stemmed Goldenrod is easily recognized from August to October by the tufts of yellow flower heads in the axils of its smooth slender leaves (6-12 cm long). These alternate leaves are sharply toothed, stalkless and taper at both ends. A white bloom covers the bluish or purplish stem, which often bends or curves to an almost horizontal position. Watch for it in woodlands and thickets in the Carolinian and southern Mixed Forest regions. (See also Zigzag Goldenrod, p. 140.)

CANADA GOLDENROD
(Solidago canadensis)

Our most common Goldenrod, its graceful yellow plumes are obvious in August and September along roadsides and in clearings or thickets throughout the Carolinian and Mixed Forest regions. Each of the small flower heads is held on the upper side of a spreading, often curved, branch. The inflorescence is about as wide as it is tall. The stems are densely leafy and smooth at the base, but downy toward the top. By flowering time the basal leaves have disappeared. The largest leaves are halfway along the stem. Two prominent veins on each side of the mid-vein are distinctive. This plant was introduced into Europe for garden cultivation.

TO 2m

3-10 dm

3-13 dm

(139)

ZIGZAG GOLDENROD
(Solidago flexicaulis)

Zigzag Goldenrod is similar to the Blue-stemmed Goldenrod in having small clusters of flower heads in the axils of the leaves and in preferring shady wooded areas in the Carolinian and southern Mixed Forests. However, the stem of the Zigzag is erect and its sharply toothed leaves are broad. This Goldenrod flowers from August to October and often forms patches where it grows. Large ray florets produce showy flower heads. The leaves decrease in size toward the top of the stem. Like the other Goldenrods, this species produces small ribbed fruits with the calyx modified into fine hairs which aid in wind dispersal.

GRASS-LEAVED GOLDENROD
(Solidago graminifolia)

It is easy to recognize a plant as a Goldenrod, but sometimes more difficult to identify it further. Grass-leaved Goldenrod is distinguished by its flat-topped inflorescence and its numerous narrow leaves with parallel veins and rough but untoothed margins. Very frequently, black spots caused by a fungal infection develop on the leaves, and serve as another identification feature. The basal leaves have been lost by flowering time (July to October). Found in moist open places such as stream banks, wet meadows, or along roadsides, this Goldenrod occurs from the Carolinian to the Boreal Forest region.

EARLY GOLDENROD
(Solidago juncea)

Early Goldenrod might be confused with Canada Goldenrod, but its largest leaves are at the base, and its tiny leaflets and shoots grow in the axils of its untoothed upper leaves. The large broad basal leaves present at flowering time have toothed margins and tapering bases. It also has less densely leafy stems than the Canada Goldenrod, and only 1 main leaf vein. Blooming from mid-July to September, the flowering heads are large with ray flowers 3-5 mm long. It grows in dry, usually open, sites and is rare in the Carolinian zone, but extends northward to the Boreal Forest.

3-12 dm

3-12 dm

3-12 dm

(140)

GREY GOLDRENROD
(Solidago nemoralis)

Often called Old Field or Dwarf Goldenrod, this species is most frequent in the dry or sandy soils of old pastures and open woods. Greyish hairs on the stems and leaves produce an overall greenish-grey effect. The largest leaves, at the base of the plant, are broadest near the tip, where they are toothed and taper to the smooth-margined base. The narrow compact inflorescence characteristically curves to one side. Grey Goldenrod flowers from late July to October and is widespread from the Carolinian zone to the southern Boreal Forest region.

ROUGH-STEMMED GOLDENROD
(Solidago rugosa)

This very variable species, which blooms from July to October, may have either a compact or widely spreading inflorescence. The hairs on the stem are visible without a magnifying lens, and the upper leaf surfaces have a sandpapery texture. Prominent veins, a wrinkled surface, deep sharp teeth, and a stalkless blade are distinctive features. The basal leaves, which may have withered by flowering time, are broader and taper to a winged stalk. The plant grows in moist or dry thickets, on slopes or banks, and along roadsides from the Carolinian zone north to the Boreal Forest region.

ELECAMPANE
(Inula helenium)

A European plant, escaped from cultivation, Elecampane is naturalized in southern Ontario in fields, waste places, and along roadsides. It blooms from July to September. There are only a few very large flowering heads on each tall plant. Many slender bright-yellow ray flowers, over 1 cm long, occur around the central orange-yellow disc (3-5 cm across). The entire flower head is surrounded by numerous leafy bracts. Broad leaves (up to 50 cm × 20 cm) are softly downy on the undersurface. The basal leaves are stalked, while the upper stalkless ones clasp the stem. In Europe the cooked roots are candied and eaten as a confection.

1-10 dm

3-15 dm

TO 2 m

(141)

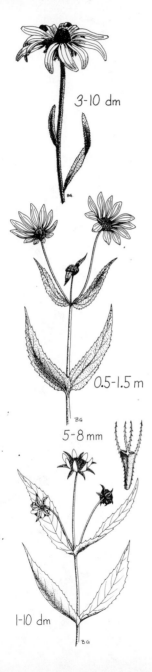

3-10 dm

0.5-1.5 m

5-8 mm

1-10 dm

BLACK-EYED SUSAN
(Rudbeckia serotina)

The large flower heads (5-8 cm), with broad yellow rays and a brown dome-shaped centre of disc florets, are seen in meadows and woodland clearings from late June to September. Bristly hairs cover the leaves and stems, giving them a rough texture. Upper stem leaves are rarely over 2 cm wide, while those at the base are slightly broader and widest near the tip. These plants have spread to the east from the Great Plains. A closely related species (*R. hirta*), native to this area and found in woods and thickets, has broader, usually coarsely toothed leaves. Both species are widespread.

WOODLAND SUNFLOWER
(Helianthus divaricatus)

The smooth stem bears opposite lance-shaped leaves 8-15 cm long and 2-7 cm broad. They are 3-nerved, thick, rough on the upper surface, hairy below, and sometimes have shallow teeth. Flowering occurs in July and August. Only a few showy heads (5 cm across) are produced from the axils of the upper leaves. Frequently found in dry open woodlands and thickets, Woodland Sunflower grows mainly in southern Ontario. The closely related Jerusalem Artichoke (*H. tuberosus*) grows in rich or damp thickets. Its leaves are like those of the cultivated Sunflower, but are without a heart-shaped base. This native plant was cultivated and highly valued by the Indians for its fleshy edible tuber.

BUR-MARIGOLD
(Bidens cernua)

Deep-yellow to golden flower heads may have up to 8 ray florets (1.7 cm) around the central disc (1.5-2.5 cm), but ray flowers are often absent. Several leafy bracts may be longer than the rays and cover the shorter inner bracts. Erect flowering heads become bent back as the fruit develops. The olive-green burs have 4 barbed spines. Bur-marigold is widespread in Ontario along edges of streams and in marshes, flowering from late July to late September.

(142)

BEGGAR'S-TICKS
(Bidens frondosa)

Also flowering in late summer and autumn, Beggar's-ticks differs from Bur-marigold in having pinnately compound leaves with 3-5 leaflets. Ray flowers are often not developed and the orange disc rarely exceeds 1 cm. The 5-8 leafy bracts surrounding the flower heads are 0.5-2 cm, but occasionally up to 6 cm long. Dark-brown to blackish fruits are flattened and have one main vein. Their 2-barbed awns allow for efficient dispersal by catching on clothing or fur. Growing in damp ground and waste places, they occur throughout much of Ontario from the Carolinian zone to the southern Boreal Forest region.

2-12 dm

5-10 mm

PINEAPPLE-WEED
(Matricaria matricarioides)

A pineapple fragrance is produced when this plant is bruised or broken. The branching stems have finely divided leaves, 1-5 cm long, and several to many small yellowish flower heads, 5-9 mm across, composed entirely of disc flowers. Blooming continues from June to October, in waste places about cities and along roadsides or paths throughout Ontario. Other members of the Aster family with similar foliage, such as Chamomile and Sneezeweed, have white ray flowers surrounding the yellow discs.

5-40 cm

COLTSFOOT
(Tussilago farfara)

Appearing first like a downy white Asparagus and then resembling a leafless Dandelion, Coltsfoot heralds the spring. The bright lemon-yellow flowers sometimes form extensive patches on moist clay slopes and stream banks. By the time the white tufts of seeds are being blown about by the wind in June, the leaves are well developed; they are up to 20 cm long with a white velvety undersurface. Since Greek and Roman times, this plant has been used to treat coughs (Tussilago means cough-dispeller) and was so well known during the Middle Ages that the leaf was the symbol painted on the herbalist's door.

7-15 cm

0.5-5 dm

(143)

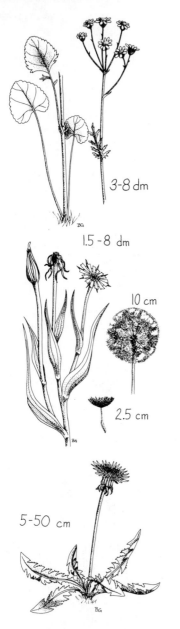

3-8 dm

1.5 - 8 dm

10 cm

2.5 cm

5-50 cm

GOLDEN RAGWORT
(*Senecio aureus*)

The golden-yellow flower heads are evident from May to July in swamps and wet meadows throughout most of Ontario. Balsam Ragwort (*S. pauperculus*) of the Mixed and Boreal Forest regions has more slender basal leaves which taper to the petiole. The weedy Common Groundsel (*S. vulgaris*) is an inconspicuous low plant of waste places and flower beds in the city. It has no showy rays, the bracts around the flower heads are black-tipped, and its leaves are jagged. All these species produce fluffy white fruiting heads.

YELLOW GOAT'S-BEARD
(*Tragopogon pratensis*)

The pale-yellow flower heads enclosed by 8 long-pointed bracts (12-24 mm) are a common sight from June to October. A white umbrella-like plume is attached to each seed. A closely related species (*T. dubuis*) has about 13 bracts which are longer than the rays and may grow to 4-7 cm by fruiting time; the stalk below the flowering or fruiting head is much expanded and hollow. The purple-flowered Salsify (*T. porrifolius*), like *T. pratensis*, has a slender uninflated stalk, but its pappus plumes are brown. Smooth grass-like leaves and a juicy milk in the stem characterizes these species, which grow in waste ground and along roadsides. All are originally from Europe.

COMMON DANDELION
(*Taraxacum officinale*)

Dandelions with showy flower heads (5 cm across) were brought to North America by early European settlers to adorn their gardens. Since dandelions are related to lettuce, it is not surprising that the young leaves make excellent salad greens. Various adapted types of this hardy widespread perennial species flourish in different habitats, ranging from damp shaded woods to dry open roadsides. Red-seeded Dandelion (*T. laevigatum*) grows in drier places and differs in having more deeply dissected leaves and reddish seeds.

FIELD SOW-THISTLE
(Sonchus arvensis)

Flat-topped inflorescences of dandelion-like flowers (3-5 cm across) appear from July to October, and glandular hairs are present on the bracts and flower-head stalks. Later, fluffy white fruiting heads are produced. The sharply lobed leaves, edged with weak spines, taper to the stem. Common Sow-thistle (*S. oleracea*) has smaller flower heads (1.5-2.5 cm) and smooth bracts and flower-head stalks. Its leaves have sharp-pointed lobes with soft spiny teeth, which surround the stem. Both these introduced species produce a white sap when their stems are broken, and their leaves can be boiled as vegetables. Sow-thistles occur in waste ground throughout Ontario.

YELLOW HAWKWEED
(Hieracium florentinum)

Numerous yellow heads (each about 2 cm across) and more or less smooth leaves with a whitish bloom are characteristic. *H. floribundum* is similar, but produces horizontal runners. *H. pratense* is hairy on the upper leaf surfaces, is without a whitish bloom, and may or may not have runners. Mouse-ear Hawkweed (*H. pilosella*) is distinctive in having larger solitary yellow heads, very leafy runners, and leaves that are white-felted beneath. These 3 species have been introduced and are now widespread. Our native yellow-flowered Hawkweeds are leafy-stemmed and less common. (See also p. 146.)

ORANGE DAY-LILY
(Hemerocallis fulva)

Hemerocallis means "beautiful for a day" and refers to the fact that the orange unspotted flowers open for a few hours on 1 day only. From May to July the 6-parted flowers (10-15 cm across) are held upright on a leafless stalk in a forking inflorescence. The 3 inner petals have wavy margins and are yellow toward the base. Escaped from cultivation, the plant often grows in dense stands along roadsides. The boiled flower buds, served with butter and green beans, are said to be delicious.

FLOWERS (YELLOW)

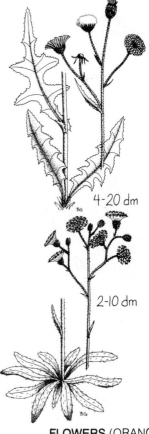

4-20 dm

2-10 dm

FLOWERS (ORANGE)

1 m

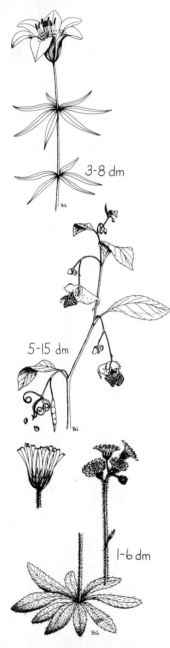

3-8 dm

5-15 dm

1-6 dm

WOOD LILY
(*Lilium philadelphicum*)

Appearing in June and July, the 1 or 2 flowers (5.5-8.5 cm) of the Wood Lily are orange to scarlet, mottled inside with purple-brown spots. They stand erect, and narrow toward the base. The smooth linear leaves, 5-10 cm, are in whorls of 4-7 at a node. The Wood Lily grows in sandy or shallow rocky soils of meadows, open woods, and dry thickets from the Carolinian zone north to the shores of James Bay.

JEWEL-WEED
(*Impatiens capensis*)

Spotted with reddish-brown on the inside, the delicate flowers, 2.5 cm long, hang on slender stalks from June to September. One of the sepals is formed into a hollow nectar-filled spur, which bends backward. Hummingbirds and bees are especially attracted to the flowers. If you touch a mature fruit pod it suddenly explodes, the rapid uncurling of the elastic partitions flinging the seeds away. This has resulted in another common name, "Touch-me-not". The juice of the stems is reputed to be a cure for Poison Ivy. Jewel-weed occurs in moist woods and swamps from the Carolinian to the Boreal Forest zones. Pale Jewel-weed (*I. pallida*) has yellow flowers with reddish spots and a short spur which points downward. Pink Jewel-weed (*I. glandulifera*), with larger pale pink to magenta flowers in August and September, has escaped from cultivation and grows in moist thickets.

ORANGE HAWKWEED
(*Hieracium aurantiacum*)

An attractive plant of roadsides, fields, and other open areas, this Eurasian species has become well established from the Carolinian to the Boreal Forest regions. The bright orange-red flower heads (2 cm across) supported on tall leafless stalks are unmistakable. Dark hairs cover the bracts that surround the flower heads, and numerous long hairs are present on the narrowly elliptical leaves (4-20 cm long), which are often broadest near the tip.

(146)

PUCCOON
(Lithospermum caroliniense)

From late May to July, bright-orange funnel-shaped flowers are crowded in leafy-bracted clusters at the tips of the stems. On stalks 5 mm long, the flowers (to 2.5 cm across) have 5 lobes with glandular hairs on the inside. By late summer the fruiting stalks may have elongated to 16 mm; they support shiny white "stone-seeds" which are actually nutlets. Short rough hairs cover the stem and stalkless narrow leaves. Found mostly in sandy soil, Puccoon grows in upland woods, in dune areas along shorelines, and on prairies.

3-6 dm

RED TRILLIUM
(Trillium erectum)

The deep reddish-purple flower nods on a slender stalk above a whorl of 3 broad leaves. An unpleasant odour is emitted, which attracts pollinators. Flowers open slightly earlier (beginning in April) than the White Trillium. Red Trillium grows mainly in moist woods in the Carolinian and Mixed Forest zones. Sometimes albino forms occur in which the petals are creamy (not pure) white, but the ovary always remains bright red. The flowers should not be confused with the pink to magenta withering flowers of the White Trillium, which are erect and have longer and wider petals, and green ovaries.

2-4 dm

WILD GINGER
(Asarum canadense)

Even during April and May when they are flowering, the softly downy, heart-shaped leaves (8-12 cm wide) are the most conspicuous part of the plant. The reddish-brown 3-parted flowers are held close to the ground on short, down-curving stalks. The colour as well as the foul smell of these hairy cup-shaped flowers attract carrion-eating beetles, which walk right into them and effect pollination. Although this is not true ginger, when the root stalk is broken it produces a gingery smell. Wild Ginger grows in southern Ontario, mainly south of the Canadian Shield, and in the Mixed Forest of northwestern Ontario.

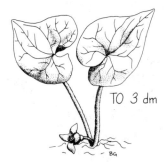

TO 3 dm

(147)

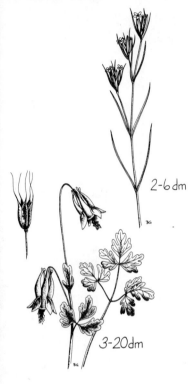

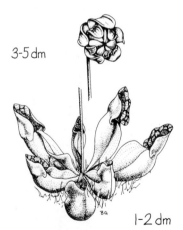

2-6 dm

3-20dm

3-5 dm

1-2 dm

DEPTFORD PINK
(Dianthus armeria)

From May to July, deep-rose flowers (2 cm across) with white-speckled centres open one at a time, and occur in clusters of 3-9 at the tips of slender branches. The needle-like leaves, up to 5 cm long, are arranged in pairs along the softly hairy stem. Deptford Pink is found throughout Ontario, especially in the Carolinian and Mixed Forest zones, in dry fields and along roadsides.

WILD COLUMBINE
(Aquilegia canadensis)

In spring, showy clusters of bright orange-red and yellow nodding flowers, each 2.5-5 cm or more, can be seen on wooded hillsides or rocky ledges and outcrops. The yellow petal blades are prolonged into hollow red spurs (1.5 to 2.5 cm long) which contain nectar available to long-tongued insects. The generic name comes from the Greek *aquila* (meaning "claws of the eagle"), referring to the shape of the flowers. Upright persisting fruits are 5-parted. Columbine occurs from the Carolinian to the Boreal Forest zone.

PITCHER-PLANT
(Sarracenia purpurea)

The hollow cup-shaped leaves of the Pitcher-plant catch and hold rainwater. Various insects are attracted to the leaves by the purple vein pattern, by the sugar secretions, or by the musty odour of the older leaves. Alighting on the flared hood at the tip of the leaf, they are directed downward by stiff hairs, and are suddenly precipitated by smooth surfaces through the narrow neck into the cavity below. The leaves release chemicals into the water, and these act as wetting agents to prevent the captured insects from escaping. Digesting substances are also released. In June and July look for unusual nodding flowers (5-7 cm across) with umbrella-shaped stigmas. Pitcher-plants grow in bogs and sandy mires; they can be found throughout Ontario, although only rarely in the Carolinian zone.

MARSH CINQUEFOIL
(Potentilla palustris)

This is an exception to the rule that cinquefoils always have yellow flowers. The reddish-purple flowers of this plant (2 cm across) appear from June to August. The 5 petals are about half as long as the broad purple sepals. Each alternate long-stalked leaf has 5-7 toothed leaflets. The thick woody stems root in the water of the marshes and swamps. Marsh Cinquefoil is found from the Mixed Forest region to the Hudson Bay Lowlands.

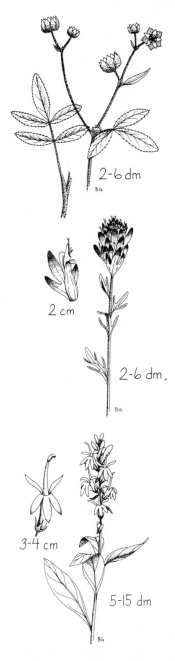

SCARLET PAINTED-CUP
(Castilleja coccinea)
Indian Paint-Brush

This is a most spectacular and unusual member of the Snapdragon family. From late May to July the orange-red (rarely yellow) tips of the 3-lobed bracts beneath each flower form the colourful part of the inflorescence. Small greenish-yellow flowers, which are narrow and have 2 lips, occur in thick spikes 4-6 cm long, but are mostly concealed by the colourful bracts. Deeply-lobed sessile leaves grow in an alternate arrangement along the hairy stem. Interestingly, this plant is a parasite on the roots of other plants. It grows along the sandy shores of L. Erie, the Bruce Peninsula and Manitoulin Island. It also occurs in meadows and moist prairies, especially in the limestone regions of southern Ontario.

CARDINAL FLOWER
(Lobelia cardinalis)

The brilliant scarlet flowers of the Cardinal Flower create a lasting impression. With an almost velvety appearance, the flowers occur in spike-like clusters (10-40 cm) from late July to September. Each flower is about 3-4 cm long and has a tube of stamens which emerges through a slit between the 2 lobes of the upper lip. The lower lip has 3 spreading lobes. The leaves (to 16 cm) and stems are smooth. Cardinal Flower grows in wet places, especially along streams in southern Ontario, and is our only red *Lobelia* sp.

(149)

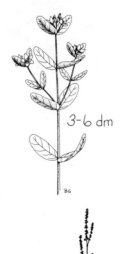

MARSH ST. JOHN'S-WORT
(*Hypericum virginicum*)

You will find this plant in bogs, swamps, marshes, and open wet sand. During July and August, 5-parted flowers occur in small clusters in the upper axils and at the top of the stem. Varying from flesh-coloured to reddish-brown, the petals are 7-10 mm long. Three orange glands alternate with 3 bundles of stamens around the pistil in the centre of the flower. Smooth, often purplish, leaves (2-6 cm) are round-tipped with dark dots beneath. This plant is rare in the Carolinian zone, but occurs more commonly in the Mixed and Boreal Forest zones.

3-6 dm

SHEEP-SORREL
(*Rumex acetosella*)

Often becoming a troublesome weed of dry lawns and fields. Sheep-sorrel is easily identified by its small arrow-shaped leaves with their spreading basal lobes. Its orange-red or yellowish branched inflorescence of minute flowers often comprises up to ½ the height of the plant; flowering occurs from June to October. The 3-angled fruits (1.5 mm) are golden brown. Sorrel means "sour or bitter tasting", and refers to the flavour of the leaves, which are said to be tasty in combination with salads and sauces. Introduced from Europe, Sheep-sorrel is now widespread, occurring in open acid sites throughout Ontario.

1-4 dm

ROSE TWISTED-STALK
(*Streptopus roseus*)

A member of the Lily family that flowers late in the spring (May-June), Rose Twisted-stalk is in many ways similar to Solomon's Seal. However, each pale-pink bell-shaped flower (1 cm) is attached opposite each leaf; the flowers do not hang in pairs from the leaf axils. The flower stalks are bent or twisted near the middle, and the stem zigzags between the alternate leaves (5-9 cm). Bright-red berries are produced in August. The plant is sparsely hairy, especially at the nodes. It grows in rich moist woods and thickets from the Carolinian zone to the Boreal Forest, and is most common in the Mixed Forest region.

3-8 dm

STEMLESS LADY'S-SLIPPER
(Cypripedium acaule)

The alternative common name, Moccasin Flower, alludes to the unusual shape of the lower petal (3.5-7 cm), a feature shared with several other kinds of Lady's-slipper orchids (see p. 128). It takes 10 years for a plant to grow from a seed to the flowering stage. Flowers appear from late May to early July. This attractive plant is local throughout much of southern Ontario, becoming more frequent in the rocky Canadian Shield region. It occurs in sphagnum bogs and dry woods, preferring acid substrates. Stemless Lady's-slipper is the provincial flower of Prince Edward Island. Queen Lady's-slipper (*C. reginae*), has pink and white flowers atop a leafy stem. It occurs in swampy places.

2-4 dm

ROSE POGONIA
(Pogonia ophioglossoides)

The petals and sepals (1.5-3 cm) are pale to deep pink, but one petal is "bearded" with yellow-tipped protuberances resembling pollen. The name *ophioglossoides* means "like a serpent's tongue". You are likely to find it with Pitcher-plants and Sundews, and with other pink orchids such as Arethusa and Grass Pink (see below) in quaking bogs and open mires, where it sometimes occurs by the hundreds. It is rare in the Carolinian zone, but more frequent northward to the Boreal Forest region. It flowers in June and July.

2-4 dm

GRASS PINK
(Calopogon tuberosus)

This remarkable flower (2.5-4 cm across) is without odour or nectar. A bee is attracted by the false promise of pollen in the yellow brush of hairs on the modified raised petal; it alights there, only to be thrown down backwards, and have the real pollen mass glued onto its back. Similarly tricked a second time by a different flower, the bee transports pollen from one flower to another. Found from southern Ontario north to the southern Boreal Forest, the Grass Pink blooms from late June to mid-July. It occurs in sphagnum bogs, marshlands, and mires.

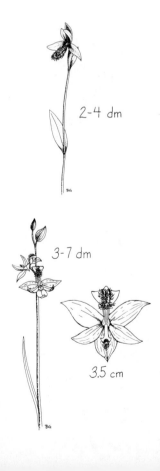

3-7 dm

3.5 cm

TO 15 dm

12-17 mm

3-6 dm

TO 5 dm

PALE SMARTWEED
(*Polygonum lapathifolium*)

Pale Smartweed is one of several Smartweeds that occur throughout much of Ontario, flowering from July to October. Spike-like flower clusters and jointed or "knotted" stems are characteristic of the group. With drooping spikes (1-8 cm) and shiny, flat, oval seeds (1.8-2.2 mm), the Pale Smartweed is found along shores, in wastelands, and in cultivated fields. Water Smartweeds (*P. natans* and *P. coccineum*) with shocking-pink flower clusters and broad floating leaves, occur in the quiet water of ditches, ponds, and slow streams. Lady's-thumb (*P. persicaria*), so named for the dark triangular blotch in the middle of the leaf, may or may not be in water. The tall (2-3 m) bamboo-like Japanese Knotweed (*P. cuspidatum*) is a weed of waste ground. (See also p. 102.)

PINK CORYDALIS
(*Corydalis sempervirens*)

It seems odd to find such a delicate plant on dry barren ridge tops. In Ontario, the Pale Corydalis occurs primarily in the Canadian Shield region. The lacy foliage is pale green. Flowers (12-17 mm), which are apparent from May to July, are pale pink to magenta with bright-yellow tips and a rounded spur at the opposite end. The Golden Corydalis (*C. aurea*) has similar foliage, but bright-yellow flowers with conspicuous spurs. It prefers open areas on limestone rocks.

BITTER-CRESS
(*Cardamine douglasii*)

The large pink patches in moist deciduous woods in early spring are usually colonies of Bitter-cress. Petals (10-16 mm) are sometimes purplish. Long slender fruits (2-3 cm) have developed by early summer. The similar Spring-cress (*C. bulbosa*) is a taller plant (20-60 cm), with smooth instead of hairy stems and white flowers with shorter petals (7-12 mm). It occurs in similar habitats, but extends farther north well into the Mixed Forest zone and flowers later (May and June).

RED CLOVER
(*Trifolium pratense*)

Like Alfalfa (see p. 162), the Red Clover is cultivated for forage and has the advantage of improving soil fertility. The pink or lavender flowers appear from May to September. Blunt oval leaves are blotched with a white V-shaped mark as in the White Clover (p. 112). Other plants of fields and meadows with similar leaves (see pp. 135-6) are without this marking. The short-stalked heads of Red Clover are closely surrounded by two 3-parted leaves, while the pink-and-white flower heads of Alsike Clover (*T. hybridum*) are long stalked. *Trifolium* refers to the 3-parted leaves, and *pratense* means "of meadows".

TO 8 dm

1-2.5 cm

TICK-TREFOIL
(*Desmodium canadense*)

Most of us become familiar with the fruit of this plant before we notice any other part of it. Unlike most other members of the Pea family, the fruit is covered with tiny hooked hairs and transversely segmented so that it separates readily into one-seeded joints (5-6.5 mm) that adhere to passing animals. These burs are produced in late summer and are particularly tenacious. Flowers (10-13 mm) appear in July and August. Tick-trefoil occurs on banks and dry sandy hills and in open woods from the Carolinian zone north to the southern Mixed Forest region.

TO 2 m

VETCHLING
(*Lathyrus palustris*)

Found along shores and in wet meadows and marshes, this plant is widely distributed in Ontario from the Carolinian zone to the Hudson Bay Lowlands. The slender climbing stems are winged. Pinkish to reddish-purple flowers (12-20 mm) are produced in groups of 2 to 6 from June to September. Another native pea, the Beach Pea (*L. japonicus*), occurs on dry sand dunes around the shores of the Great Lakes, Lake Nipissing, and James Bay. Its stems are not winged, and its thick fleshy leaflets are oval with large arrow-shaped stipules at the base.

TO 1m

(153)

TO 6 dm

3-7dm

8-15 cm

HERB ROBERT
(Geranium robertianum)

It is possible to find a flowering specimen of Herb Robert from May to October, but the small pink or reddish-purple flowers (10-15 mm across) are most numerous in June and July. Often abundant in damp rich woods, Herb Robert occurs from the Carolinian zone north to the southern Mixed Forest region. It was named for the Benedictine monk, St. Robert. The lacy fern-like leaves are readily distinguished from ferns by the soft downy hairs on the leaf stalks and, of course, by the absence of spores on the under surface of the leaf. The leaves of the similar Bicknell's Geranium (*G. bicknellii*) are merely deeply cleft instead of compound. It is found in drier and more open habitats.

WILD GERANIUM
(Geranium maculatum)

Flowering in May and June, the Wild Geranium is common in rich woods of the Carolinian zone, though northward it becomes rare. The pink to rose-purple and occasionally white flowers are 2.5-4 cm across. *Geranos* is the Greek word for "crane", and refers here to the long slender fruit reminiscent of a crane's bill. This fruit, which splits into five segments, separating and curling back at the base, is characteristic of the Geranium family.

FRINGED POLYGALA
(Polygala pauciflora)

The broad evergreen leaves are sometimes mistaken for those of Wintergreen (p. 118). Rose-purple or sometimes white flowers (1.5-2.3 cm long), which appear in May and June, remind one of orchid blossoms. The succulent appendage on the end of the seed is attractive to ants, which use the oil that it contains as a food source. They carry the seeds to their underground chambers, remove the appendage and discard the seeds, which are thus not only distributed over short distances but also planted by ants. Seeds are probably dispersed over greater distances by birds. Fringed Polygala occurs in deciduous and mixed woods from the Carolinian zone north to the Hudson Bay Lowlands.

MUSK MALLOW
(*Malva moschata*)

The introduced Musk Mallow was once widely cultivated as an ornamental. It is now less popular in cultivation but is locally common along road-sides and in waste places, especially in limestone regions. Pink or white flowers with triangular petals (2.5-3 cm long) and a musty odour appear from June to September. Mallows are closely related to Hollyhocks, also once very popular in the garden, and like them have numerous stamens forming a column in the centre of the flower. The Velvet-leaf, Butterprint, or Elephant's-ear (*Abutilon theophrastis*) has structurally similar yellow flowers. Reaching 2 m in height and with large, heart-shaped, velvety leaves, it is an impressive introduced weed, common in the cultivated lands of extreme south-western Ontario.

COMMON MALLOW
(*Malva neglecta*)

A weedy creeping mallow of gardens, lawns, and waste places, especially along the edges of sidewalks and fences, the Common Mallow was introduced from Europe. Small flowers with petals about 1 cm long appear from May to October. They may be pinkish, lavender, pale bluish (lilac), or white: always a problem in field guides based upon flower colour. The ring of 12-15 one-seeded carpels resembles a circle of cheese wedges, hence the common name "Cheeses".

PURPLE LOOSESTRIFE
(*Lythrum salicaria*)

This aggressive introduced plant may become dominant in wet meadows and ditches. Such places are aglow with purplish-red flowers in late summer. Three kinds of flowers are produced, each differing in the length of the styles and filaments of the anthers. The petals are 7-10 mm long and the flowering spikes may reach 30 cm or more. The species name *salicaria* means "like a willow" (*Salix*) and refers to the shape of the leaves. Purple Loosestrife is widespread in Ontario.

4-10 dm

1-6 dm

6 mm

6-12 dm

0.8-1 mm

TO 2 m

TO 2.5 dm

1.5 dm

3-12 dm

FIREWEED
(Epilobium angustifolium)

There is still disagreement as to how the name "Fireweed" originated. Some say it is because the plants grow in such quantity in recently burned areas; others say it is because the masses of flowers appearing in mid-summer on long spikes and waving in the breeze resemble a fire. In late summer and autumn the slender fruits (3-8 cm) split open to release numerous tiny seeds. Each seed has a tuft of long silky white hairs, which aid in dispersal over great distances. Thousands of plants releasing seeds simultaneously gives the impression of smoke. Fireweed is found throughout Ontario, but is more frequent in the north. The introduced Hairy Willow Herb (*E. hirsutum*) is common in swamps and marshes in southern Ontario. It has mostly opposite toothed leaves and shallowly notched petals.

BIRD'S-EYE PRIMROSE
(Primula mistassinica)

This is one of the less common species in this book. Large patches of the small pink flowers (1-2 cm across), with yellow "eyes" in the centre, brighten the upper Lake Huron shores in late spring and early summer, a time when few other shoreline wildflowers are blooming.

SPREADING DOGBANE
(Apocynum androsaemifolium)

A somewhat poisonous milky fluid is produced by this relative of the Milkweed family. Because of the high latex content it was investigated as a substitute for rubber during the Second World War. Flowering in summer, Spreading Dogbane occurs in dry open habitats throughout much of central and northern Ontario. The bell-shaped flowers (6-10 mm long) are pinkish but marked with red inside. The similar Indian Hemp (*A. cannabinum*) has smaller flowers (3-6 mm) which are white or greenish-white, and the soft hairs on its seeds are 2-3 cm instead of 1-2 cm long. Fibres of the Indian Hemp were used by the Indians to produce a thread which could be woven into fishing lines, and rope.

(156)

COMMON MILKWEED
(*Asclepias syriaca*)

A common native plant of roadsides and meadows, Milkweed blooms from late June to August. Many pale-pink or purplish flowers (8-10 mm) in large clusters of 20-40 attract pollinating insects, but only one or two of these flowers become puffy ripened seed pods (10 cm long) containing numerous silky tufted seeds. Swamp Milkweed (*A. incarnata*) prefers moist situations and has narrower leaves, darker purple-pink flowers, and more slender smooth fruiting pods. A number of insects, including beetles, bugs, butterflies, and moths, feed on the various species of Milkweeds. Our large orange Monarch Butterfly is a good example. All these insects are brightly and distinctively coloured; predators can therefore more easily associate the colouring with their frequently bitter taste inherited from the poisonous plant juices.

MOTHERWORT
(*Leonurus cardiaca*)

The two-lipped flowers (1 cm long) are arranged in dense clusters in the axils of the leaves. This feature as well as the opposite leaves and square stem is characteristic of the Mint family. Motherwort is introduced from Asia and was once cultivated for its medicinal properties. Flowering from June to August, it occurs in open woods, especially along paths and in wastelands.

WILD BERGAMOT
(*Monarda fistulosa*)

Wild Bergamot occurs on dry hills, banks, and woodland edges throughout much of Ontario. The name *fistulosa* means "tubular" and refers to the shape of the flowers (2-3 cm), which appear from late June to September. In addition to opposite leaves and square stems, it possesses the minty odour so characteristic of the Mint family. Scarlet Beebalm (*M. didyma*) is closely related, but readily distinguished by its larger red flowers. It grows in moist woods and along stream banks in southern Ontario.

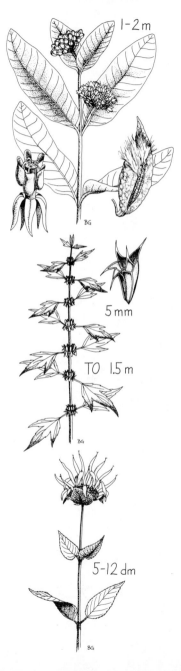

HAIRY BEARD-TONGUE
(Penstemon hirsuta)

Although it has opposite leaves and 2-lipped flowers, this plant is without square stems and aromatic foliage and is not a member of the Mint family. It belongs instead with the Snapdragon group. Pinkish-purple flowers (2-3 cm long), with white lobes, open in late May, and in June and July. Capsules, 8-9 mm long, develop with persisting styles in late summer. The stems and the inflorescence branches are covered with fine gland-tipped hairs. Look for this plant in dry woods, thickets, fields, and open rocky places in the Carolinian and southern Mixed Forest regions.

SLENDER GERARDIA
(Gerardia tenuifolia)

Found in moist shoreline meadows and low spots in sandy fields, the Slender Gerardia is an attractive late summer and autumn wildflower. The flowers, 1-1.5 cm long, are usually borne in opposite pairs on branching stems; the flower stalks are longer than the flowers. With larger rose-purple flowers (1.5-4 cm) and shorter stalks, the Purple Gerardia (*G. purpurea*) occurs in similar habitats but is less common.

TWINFLOWER
(Linnaea borealis)

Twinflower occurs in cool, moist, shady woods from the Mixed Forest zone north to James Bay. In fact various subspecies of Twinflower occur in boreal forests throughout the Northern Hemisphere. A delicate and beautiful wildflower, it was a favourite of the great Swedish botanist, Carolus Linnaeus, who is commemorated in the genus name. The shiny oval leaves are evergreen. Erect stems usually support 2 flowers, but sometimes stems with 1 or 3 are found. The pink or white funnel-shaped flowers (10-15 mm long) appear on nodding hairy stalks from June to August. They are similar to those of Honeysuckle, and Twinflower does belong to the Honeysuckle family (p. 93), a group comprised mostly of shrubby plants.

TEASEL
(Dipsacus sylvestris)

Some species of Teasel have been extensively cultivated for the dry spiny fruit heads which were used to raise the nap (comb up the fine hairy surface) on woollen cloth. From July to September, the pinkish tubular flowers open first about the middle of the egg-shaped flower heads (5-10 cm long) forming a ring which gradually spreads up and down. The prickly stems and spiny fruit heads persist all winter, and are gathered for dry bouquets. Teasel occurs throughout southern Ontario in neglected pastures and along grassy roadsides.

SPOTTED JOE-PYE-WEED
(Eupatorium maculatum)

Blooming in late summer, this plant forms large patches along the margins of bogs, streams, and wet meadows. Joe-Pye is reported to have been an 18th century North American Indian who cured typhoid with an extract of this plant. The Green-stemmed Joe-Pye-weed (*E. purpureum*) differs in having a rounded rather than a flat-topped inflorescence, and 3-7 florets per head instead of 8-20. In addition, *E. purpureum* is whitish-green between the nodes instead of purple or purple-spotted, and the crushed foliage has a distinct vanilla odour. *E. maculatum* grows throughout much of Ontario, but is most frequent in the Mixed Forest region; *E. purpureum* occurs in the Carolinian zone.

BLAZING STAR
(Liatris cylindracea)

The Blazing Stars, uncommon in Ontario, are a group of plants preferring more or less dry open ground. Distinguished by its plumed (*i.e.* branched) pappus, *L. cylindracea* occurs on open sand dunes and limestone prairie. It is locally common along the Lake Huron shore south of Grand Bend. The much taller (to 1.8 m) *L. spicata* occurs in tall grass prairies of the extreme southwest. These species bloom in late summer, and with the other showy prairie blossoms make up some of our most dramatic wildflower displays.

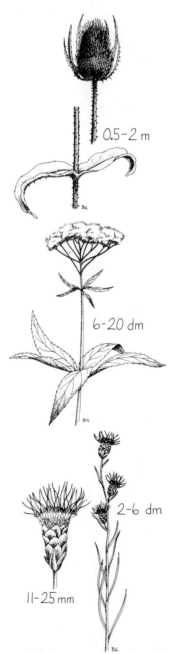

0.5-2 m

6-20 dm

2-6 dm

11-25 mm

(159)

TO 1.5 m

COMMON BURDOCK
(*Arctium minus*)

Flowering from late July to September, Burdock occurs in wastelands, fields, and open woods, and along roadsides throughout most of Ontario. Each flowering head (1.5-2.5 cm across) is surrounded by numerous bristle-like hooked bracts. When the seeds have ripened, the entire heads become easily dislodged and cling to fur or clothing, thus aiding in dispersal of the seeds. Compare this with other burs on p. 134. The foliage of Burdock is often mistaken for Rhubarb, but the hollow leaf stalks are not red and the lower leaf surface is white-woolly. Distinguished by its larger flowering heads (2.5 cm or more) on longer stalks, the Great Burdock (*A. lappa*) is also an introduced weed but is less common.

3-10 dm

NODDING THISTLE
(*Carduus nutans*)

Nodding Thistle often becomes a conspicuous plant in dry pasture lands, where the livestock avoid its spiny-lobed leaves. The bright pinkish-purple flower heads (4.5-7 cm across) are surrounded by broad spiny-tipped bracts, and the lower main stems are leafy-winged. Since the pappus is not finely divided (plumose), the name Plumeless Thistle is often given to members of this genus. Introduced from Eurasia, Nodding Thistle occurs throughout southern Ontario, flowering from June to October.

3-15 dm

FIELD THISTLE
(*Cirsium arvense*)

Although often called Canada Thistle, this species was introduced from Eurasia. It is now a common plant throughout much of Ontario in fields and pastures, along roadsides, and in wastelands and gardens. Field Thistle reproduces by horizontal roots as well as by seed. The flower heads are 5-15 mm broad and 10-20 mm long. Several varieties have been recognized on the basis of differences in leaf lobing and hairiness. The native Swamp Thistle (*C. muticum*) of moist ground is a larger plant (to 3 m) with flowering heads 2-3.5 cm long and much-divided leaves that are white and cobwebby beneath.

(160)

BULL THISTLE
(Cirsium vulgare)

A spiny plant similar to Field Thistle, the Bull Thistle may be distinguished by its more slender leaf lobes, by the covering of short sharp prickles on the upper surface of the leaf blade, and by its larger flowering heads (2.5-7.5 cm across). It occurs throughout much of Ontario in pastures and waste places, flowering from July to September.

PHILADELPHIA FLEABANE
(Erigeron philadelphicus)

The flower heads (12-25 mm across) are composed of a central portion of yellow disc flowers surrounded by numerous pinkish (rarely white) ray flowers. Other common Fleabanes are usually annual instead of perennial and have a shorter pappus on the ray flowers (less than 1 mm). Daisy Fleabane (*E. annuus*) has broadly ovate, coarsely toothed and long-stalked basal leaves, and long hairs on the mid-stem; Rough Daisy Fleabane (*E. strigosus*) has fewer, narrower, and sparsely-toothed leaves, and shorter flat-lying hairs on the mid-stem. Fleabanes differ from asters in having narrower involucral bracts of uniform length in a single row and in flowering earlier (spring and early summer). The name Fleabane is derived from the notion that the plants can be used to repel fleas. Fleabanes occur in a variety of open habitats throughout Ontario.

TRAILING ARBUTUS
(Epigaea repens)

Mayflower

Flowering from April to June, Trailing Arbutus is one of the first wildflowers to appear after the snow has gone from the open woods and sphagnum bogs of the Canadian Shield region. It is rare south of the Canadian Shield. In New England, Trailing Arbutus was once so popular that it was collected in great quantity for sale and, as a result, became very scarce. It is now protected in several north-eastern states and is the provincial flower of Nova Scotia. *Epi* means "on", *gaea* means "the ground", and *repens* means "creeping".

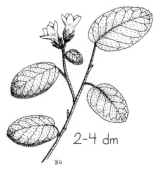

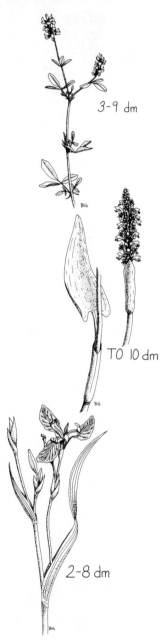

3-9 dm

TO 10 dm

2-8 dm

ALFALFA
(Medicago sativa)

The roots of Alfalfa and some other members of the Pea family have swellings produced by nitrogen-fixing bacteria which convert nitrogen in the air to nitrates in the soil, thereby increasing soil fertility. Introduced from Asia, Alfalfa is planted to improve soils and is also used as fodder. It is often found growing without cultivation along roadsides and in wastelands. Blue or occasionally purplish or pinkish flowers (8-12 mm) appear in June and July. The distinctive corkscrew-shaped fruits are finely hairy.

PICKEREL WEED
(Pontederia cordata)

Pickerel Weed is most common in the eastern parts of the Canadian Shield region west to Algoma and north to Cochrane. It often occurs in great masses in still water of coves and bays, and is frequently encountered along the edges of streams and ponds. The 6-parted flowers with yellow markings on the upper lobes are arranged in dense spikes (5-15 cm long) subtended by a bladeless sheath. Flowering occurs from July to September.

BLUE FLAG
(Iris versicolor)

Found in a variety of wetland habitats ranging from roadside ditches to marshes and shorelines, Blue Flag is widespread in Ontario from the Carolinian zone to the Boreal Forest region. Flowers (6-8 cm) are large and showy. The 3 petals are held erect while the 3 broad sepals spread horizontally with petal-like style branches covering their bases. The position of the stamens and stigma prevents self-pollination. The green fruit (3.5-5.5 cm long) is 3-angled and produces floating seeds. Dwarf Lake Iris (I. lacustris), often less than 10 cm high, blooms in May and June along the shores of L. Huron. The introduced Yellow Iris (I. pseudacorus) has escaped from cultivation to moist habitats throughout southern Ontario. It has larger capsules (5-8.5 cm long) and blooms in June.

COMMON BLUE-EYED GRASS
(Sisyrinchium montanum)

Although these plants may not look like members of the Iris family, they have the characteristic spathes subtending the flowers, 3 stamens, a 3-celled capsule, and floral parts that are attached to the top of the ovary. The delicate flowers (8-12 mm across) with yellow centres appear from June to mid-July. Common Blue-eyed Grass occurs in meadows, ditches, and along shores from the Carolinian zone north into the southern Boreal Forest region. Slender Blue-eyed Grass (*S. mucronatum*) is found along the shores of eastern L. Erie and L. Huron. It has purple instead of green spathes, and the ripened capsules are less than 3.5 mm long.

1-5 dm

TUFTED VETCH
(Vicia cracca)

This is a common plant of roadsides and fields throughout most of Ontario. It makes good hay, and like other members of the Pea family it enriches the soil by building up nitrates. The bluish flowers (9-13 mm long) appear from June to August and are attractive to bees, providing them with abundant nectar. Tufted Vetch is introduced from Europe, where it is cultivated as an ornamental and a fodder plant.

TO 1m

LONG-SPURRED VIOLET
(Viola rostrata)

The long slender spur (9-15 mm long) and pale-blue flowers with a central deep violet spot are distinctive features of this leafy-stemmed blue Violet. It occurs in rich woods of southern Ontario south and east of the Canadian Shield region, flowering from mid-April to early June and sometimes again in the fall. Three other "stemmed" blue violets found in Ontario have shorter spurs (8 mm or less). Of these, the Hooked-spur Violet (*V. adunca*) and the Dog Violet (*V. conspersa*) are widespread. The former is distinguished from the latter by its deep-blue instead of pale flowers, thicker leaves, and narrower stipules. Many violets (see also pp. 112, 137) produce inconspicuous non-opening flowers during the summer.

5-25 cm

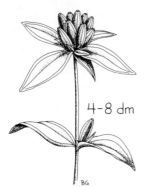

CLOSED GENTIAN
(Gentiana andrewsii)

This attractive plant is sometimes called the Bottle Gentian. Its deep-blue flowers (3.5-4 cm long) never open fully. When the flowers are forced open, the petals are seen to be joined by a fringed membrane. The flowers appear in late August and September. A plant of moist open places, it is confined in Ontario mainly to regions south of the Canadian Shield. White-flowered forms are rare.

4-8 dm

BG

FRINGED GENTIAN
(Gentianella crinita ssp. *crinita)*

A small meadow of Fringed Gentians, sapphire or sky blue, rivals any autumn scene in its beauty. The magnificent flowers (1-5.5 cm high) have delicate fringes (2-6 mm long) on their petals which spread open in the sunshine. The larger mid-stem leaves are ovate, 2-5 times as long as wide (and usually more than 8 mm wide). The Narrow-leaved Fringed Gentian (*G. crinitia* ssp. *procera*) has much narrower mid-stem leaves usually over 6 times as long as wide (rarely exceeding 8 mm wide). It is often difficult to decide to which subspecies very small plants belong, but they appear to grow from seed of the current year and there is often a larger parent plant nearby with which they can be associated. Both subspecies occur in moist open calcium-rich soils, but in Ontario the subspecies *procera* is essentially restricted to the shores of L. Huron, while the subspecies *crinita* has a more general distribution in southern Ontario exclusive of the Canadian Shield region.

3-8 dm

BG

WILD BLUE PHLOX
(Phlox divaricata)

Blooming from mid-May to late June, Wild Blue Phlox is found in moist deciduous woodlands, in clearings, and along woodland edges. In Ontario it occurs to the south and east of the Canadian Shield region. The flowers (2-3 cm across), with their notched petals, are usually pale bluish, but occasionally reddish purple or pale pink or white.

3-5 dm

BG

FORGET-ME-NOT
(Myosotis laxa)

A fair lady and her lover were walking by a river, when they saw some sweet blue flowers on a steep and dangerous bank. The lady asked for them, and the young man without hesitation went to gather them for his sweetheart, but he slipped and fell into the fast-flowing stream. As he was swept away, he tossed the flowers ashore and called "Forget-me-not!" This pretty and delicate wildflower surely ought to be part of a romantic story, whether or not the common name really had its origin in the riverside episode. The flowers (3-6 mm across) have 5 sky blue petals surrounding a yellow centre, and the tips of the inflorescence have the characteristic curl of the Borage family. Blooming mainly in June and July, it occurs in a variety of moist habitats. The introduced European Forget-me-not (*M. scorpioides*) has larger flowers (6-9 mm across) and an angled stem.

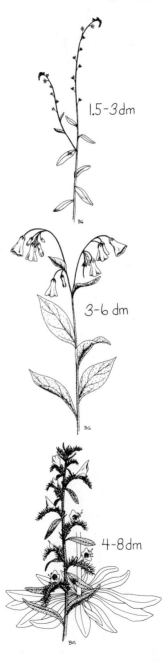

1.5-3dm

3-6 dm

4-8dm

NORTHERN BLUEBELL
(Mertensia paniculata)

From the L. Superior region northward, this attractive Bluebell may be found along moist shores and stream sides. Flowers (4.5-7 mm long) appear in June and July. The buds are pink but the mature flowers are sky blue. Virginia Bluebell (*M. virginica*), with larger flowers (10-20 mm long), is an uncommon plant of rich river bottoms in the Carolinian zone. It blooms in May and early June.

BLUEWEED
(Echium vulgare)

An introduced rough-bristly and silvery-green plant, it is often abundant in dry stony pastures and gravelly roadsides. The blue flowers with projecting red stamens appear from June to September. Another common name is Viper's Bugloss. The first word is said to be derived from the plant's use in treating the bite of the poisonous European Viper (a snake); the second is from the Greek *bouglossos*, meaning "ox-tongued", a reference to the rough leaves.

BLUE VERVAIN
(Verbena hastata)

Bluish-purple tubular flowers (3-4.5 mm across) open several at a time, the bloom progressing up the spike. The leaves are mostly lance-shaped, despite the specific name *hastata*, which means "arrow-shaped". The four-sided stems are rough-hairy. Blue Vervain is found in moist thickets, meadows, and swamps from the Carolinian zone to the southern Boreal Forest region. It flowers from June to September.

COMMON SKULLCAP
(Scutellaria galericulata)

A non-aromatic member of the Mint family, the Common Skullcap occurs in low marshy ground from the Carolinian zone to the southern Boreal Forest region. Two-lipped blue flowers (1.5-2 cm) appear in July and August. The sepals form a short tube that is partially 2-lipped, with a hollow projection on the upper lip giving the impression of a cap. The leaves are 2-5 cm long and more or less stalkless. Mad-dog Skullcap (*S. lateriflora*) has smaller flowers (5-9 mm long) on one-sided racemes arising from the axils of broader, stalked, opposite leaves. It occurs in moist habitats throughout most of Ontario.

CATNIP
(Nepeta cataria)

Catnip is introduced from Eurasia. It has become a common plant of roadsides and waste places, and may be found throughout most of Ontario. The strong minty odour makes cats ecstatically happy and energetic. The entire plant is softly greyish downy, and like most mints it has a square stem and opposite leaves. A tea made from the dried leaves is reported to act as a sedative and to relieve various digestive disorders. Candied catnip leaves have been recommended as an interesting alternative to after-dinner mints. The purplish-blue or whitish 2-lipped flowers (10-12 mm long) are spotted with deep pink or purple. Flowering occurs from July to September.

HEAL-ALL
(Prunella vulgaris)
Self-heal

This plant was once applied to a variety of wounds to stop bleeding and speed healing. Note the opposite leaves, square stems, and dense flower spikes (2-5 cm long) with prominent green or purplish-green kidney-shaped bracts. The 2-lipped flowers are mainly blue or purplish, but the central lobe of the lower lip is often whitish and fringed, giving the flower an orchid-like appearance. Flowering continues from June to September. Heal-all is a common plant throughout much of Ontario. Look for it along paths and roadsides, and in meadows and wastelands.

FIELD MINT
(Mentha arvensis)

A native species of moist shores, meadows, and ditches, Field Mint occurs throughout most of Ontario. We often first notice the pungent minty odour and then, looking down, see crushed plants underfoot. The bluish or purplish, rarely pink or white, flowers (4-7 mm long) may be seen from July to September. The fruit ripens into four 1-seeded nutlets, a universal characteristic of the Mint family. Introduced Peppermints and Spearmints have locally escaped from cultivation, but these have flowers in spikes.

MONKEY-FLOWER
(Mimulus ringens)

Although the stem is square and the flowers are prominently two-lipped, Monkey-flower produces capsules (1-1.5 cm long) rather than four 1-seeded nutlets, and is therefore not a member of the Mint family. The long styles persist after the petals have fallen. These features are characteristic of members of the Snapdragon family. Flowers appear from late June to August. *Ringens*, meaning "gaping", refers to the open lips of the deep blue, or rarely pinkish, or white corolla (2-3.5 cm long). Monkey-flower grows along moist peaty lake shores, river banks, and ditches throughout most of Ontario.

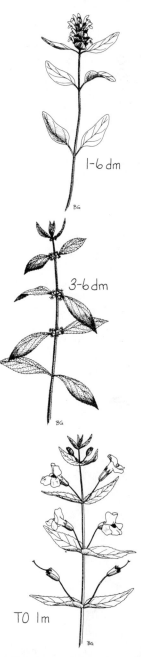

1-6 dm

BG

3-6 dm

BG

TO 1m

BG

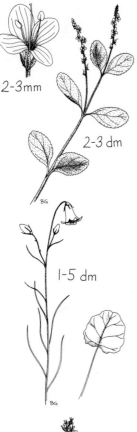

2-3mm

2-3 dm

1-5 dm

TO I m

COMMON SPEEDWELL
(*Veronica officinalis*)

The flat heart-shaped fruit (3-4 mm long), often with the style persisting between the lobes, is characteristic of the various species of Speedwells (*Veronica*). Pale-blue (less often white) flowers appear from late May to July. Common Speedwell is a hairy creeping plant with erect flower spikes arising from the leaf axils. It may be found in a variety of habitats including dry meadows and pastures, woodlands, and rocky places. Its Ontario range includes the Carolinian and southern Mixed Forest regions. American Brooklime (*V. americana*) is a closely related but non-hairy plant of moist places. Its more roundish fruits are smaller (2-3 mm) and the flowers are distinctly stalked. It occurs throughout much of Ontario, flowering from late June to August.

ROUND-LEAVED BLUEBELL
(*Campanula rotundifolia*)

This pretty wildflower is found in open woods, on rocky cliffs, and on open rocky barrens, from the Carolinian zone to the Hudson Bay Tundra region. Drooping bell-shaped flowers (1.5-3 cm long) appear from June to September. The round basal leaves, giving rise to the specific name *rotunifolia*, have often withered by flowering time. The Creeping Bellflower (*C. rapunculoides*) is an introduced species widely escaped from cultivation in southern Ontario. It has similar flowers (2-3 cm), but the leaves are triangular or lance shaped, and sandpapery.

INDIAN TOBACCO
(*Lobelia inflata*)

Although it may have some medicinal value, and the common name implies that it can be smoked, it is a poisonous plant; when taken internally it has caused coma and death. Pale blue flowers (7-10 mm), appearing from late July to September, are rather inconspicuous. The fruit ripens into an inflated oval capsule, hence the specific name *inflata*. Indian Tobacco grows in dry open fields and woods and on rocky slopes in the Carolinian and Mixed Forest regions.

GREAT LOBELIA
(Lobelia siphilitica)

A tall conspicuous plant of swamps, shores, and wet meadows, the Great Lobelia occurs in the Carolinian and southern Mixed Forest regions. The blue, rarely white, flowers (2.5 to 3.5 cm long) appear mostly from July to September. Hairy leaves (2-6 cm wide) are narrowed to a stalkless base. The species name *siphilitica* records the fact that the plant was once used in the treatment of syphilis. The smaller (to 40 cm) Kalm's Lobelia (*L. kalmii*) has blue flowers (7-16 mm), marked centrally with white, and linear leaves. It is found in moist limy meadows and on limestone cliffs and shores.

HEART-LEAVED ASTER
(Aster cordifolius)

Heart-shaped Aster is one of several species in which the basal leaves are larger than the leaves above, and have distinctive heart-shaped or flattened bases. Unlike the others in this group, it is without winged leaf stalks and most of the stem leaves also have cordate bases with characteristically rounded sinuses. In addition, the larger leaf blades are less than twice as long as they are wide, and are generally less than 8 cm in width. Flowering from late August to October, Heart-shaped Aster grows in open woods, clearings, and meadows from the Carolinian zone to the southern Mixed Forest region.

SMOOTH ASTER
(Aster laevis)

Although the basal leaves are larger than the leaves above, they are not cordate but taper gradually to winged stalks and clasping bases. The bluish-green colour and fleshy texture of these strap-shaped leaves are distinctive features. Both the leaves and stems often have a whitish bloom. The 15-30 ray flowers (8-15 mm long) are blue; the disc flowers are bright yellow. A plant of woodland edges, sand dunes, moist meadows, and prairie-like habitats, Smooth Aster occurs mainly in the Carolinian and southern Mixed Forest regions.

5-15 dm

2.5 cm

2-12 dm

3-10 dm

(169)

2-12 dm

1-6 dm

3-20 dm

LARGE-LEAVED ASTER
(Aster macrophyllus)

Large-leaved Aster is unique in having very large heart-shaped basal leaves (8-20 cm wide). Many plants often grow together in large patches, producing leaves but no flowers. The long involucre (7 mm high) and flat-topped sticky inflorescence are also characteristic. The 9-20 ray flowers (7-15 mm long) are pale blue or white, while the disc flowers become reddish. An autumn-flowering species of woodlands and clearings, Large-leaved Aster occurs throughout most of Ontario.

BOG ASTER
(Aster nemoralis)

Flowering a little earlier than most Asters, from late July to early September, Bog Aster is common in the Canadian Shield region, but rather uncommon elsewhere. It grows in acid sphagnum bogs and along rocky or sandy lake shores. Numerous linear stem leaves (12-50 mm long) and one or two large flowering heads (2.5-4 cm across) with bluish-purple rays are distinctive features to look for.

NEW ENGLAND ASTER
(Aster novae-angliae)

Just before the forests turn red and gold, the fields, meadows, and woodland clearings stage a final blaze of colour, including all shades of blues and purples as well as the yellows and white. The blue and purple autumn wildflowers so dominant in the countryside are the various species of Asters. New England Aster is one of the most showy, with large clusters of flower heads: the rays (1-2 cm long) varying from blue to purple or deep pink, and the disc flowers from yellow to orange-yellow. Basal leaves are absent at flowering time, and the upper leaves are crowded. It is common along roadsides and fencerows, and in pastures and meadows of the Carolinian and Mixed Forest regions. Flowers appear from mid-August to October. (See also *A. puniceus*, p. 171; *A.* × *amethystinus*, p. 123.)

SWAMP ASTER
(Aster puniceus)

This Aster is similar to the New England Aster but it has less crowded leaves which are toothed (although sometimes sparsely and shallowly), and its ray flowers (8-15 mm long) are pale blue instead of deep blue. It is almost always found in moist ground and wet meadows, whereas New England Aster is a plant of dry meadows and well-drained sites. Swamp Aster flowers in August and September from the Carolinian zone to the Boreal Forest.

CHICORY
(Cichorium intybus)

A coffee substitute can be made from the roasted roots of Chicory, which are used commercially in coffee blending. Chicory is said to be unexcelled as a spring green. Since it is an aggressive and a widespread introduced plant of wastelands, roadsides and pastures, there is no reason why we should not collect it. The showy sky blue flowers (to 4 cm across) are made up exclusively of broad strap-like ray flowers.

WILD BLUE LETTUCE
(Lactuca biennis)

This plant is closely related to the Dandelions, Goat's-beards, Sow-thistles and Hawkweeds, and like all of them it contains a milky juice. Watch for it in meadows and woodland clearings, and along woodland edges and stream banks. Bluish to white (rarely yellow) flowers (8-14 mm) appear from July to August. The small fruits or achenes (4-5.5 mm), with beige-brown tufts of hairs (pappus), are apparent in late summer and autumn. Wild Canada Lettuce (*L. canadensis*) has yellow flowers and beaked achenes (4.5-6.5 mm long) with a white pappus. It occurs in dry sandy places and along roadsides. The introduced Prickly Lettuce (*L. serriola*), also with yellow flowers, is a weed of roadsides and wastelands. It is prickly on the lower midrib of the lower leaves and along the leaf margins. Some species of *Prenanthes* (see p. 126) are similar, but they have triangular leaves with fewer lobes, and nodding flowers.

0.5-2.5 dm

3-17 dm

10-14 mm

6-20 dm

(171)

FLOWERS (GREEN)

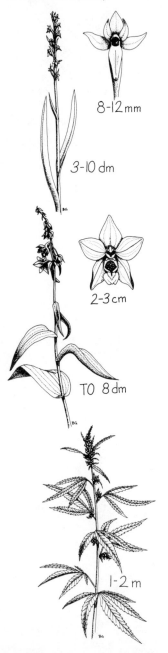

8-12 mm

3-10 dm

2-3 cm

TO 8 dm

1-2 m

TALL NORTHERN GREEN ORCHID
(*Platanthera hyperborea*)

The Tall Northern Green Orchid is one of our most abundant and widespread native orchids, although it is readily overlooked. It occurs in a great variety of habitats from swamps, marshes, and spongy alder thickets to dry sandy woods and recently abandoned gravel pits. The tongue-shaped lower petal is 4-7 mm long with a backward projecting spur of approximately the same length. The flowers open in late June and July.

HELLEBORINE
(*Epipactis helleborine*)

From localized areas near Toronto and Syracuse prior to 1900, this introduced orchid has spread widely in the northeast. It is now a common plant in southern Ontario, often growing with our native woodland plants as if it had been here all the time. It sometimes appears in gardens and lawns. Green and reddish-purple flowers with a distinctive bowl-shaped lower petal appear from July to September, and occasionally until November.

MARIJUANA
(*Cannabis sativa* ssp. *sativa*)

Although best known today as the source of the drugs marijuana and hashish, Hemp, as it is also called, was cultivated by the Chinese more than 4500 years ago for its very tough fibres. These were used in weaving mats, baskets, and ropes. The early North American colonists also grew it for making cordage and thread. In Ontario, Marijuana is a weed of wastelands, roadsides, and open sandy ground in the southern parts of the province. Our plants are apparently derived from the earlier cultivated stock which was selected for its fibre and oil qualities. These plants are only weakly intoxicant compared with the ssp. *indica* of warmer climates. Each plant is either male or female. The coarsely toothed leaflets (5-15 cm long) are more or less long-tapered to the tip.

(172)

STINGING NETTLE
(Urtica dioica ssp. *gracilis)*

Brittle hairs covering the lower leaf surfaces of this plant act like minute hypodermic needles: when the plant is touched, a chemical is dispensed beneath the skin, resulting in an immediately painful sting. This is followed by reddish swelling, continued itching, and numbness of the sensitized areas for several minutes to a few hours. Pollen is shed in large amounts from minute 4-parted flowers and contributes to summer hay fever. On the positive side, the young leaves are reported to make an excellent potherb, and good yields of high quality "hay" are obtained from Stinging Nettle in Russia. Most common in southern Ontario, Stinging Nettles occur in rich moist soil and are often encountered about compost dumps. The rarer European subspecies *dioica* has wide leaves, a more branching growth habit, and its stinging hairs are not confined to the lower leaf surface. The Wood-nettle (*Laportea canadensis*) belongs to the same family and also has stinging hairs. Widespread in southern Ontario, in low-lying woods and along banks of streams, it is readily distinguished from Stinging Nettle by its alternate leaves and 5-parted flowers.

FALSE NETTLE
(Boehmeria cylindrica)

False Nettle differs from the stinging species (above) in having an unbranched spike-like inflorescence. It occurs in swampy woods in southern Ontario, mainly south of the Canadian Shield, and flowers in July and August.

CURLY DOCK
(Rumex crispus)

A common introduced plant of moist meadows, shorelines, and roadside ditches, Curly Dock may be found throughout most of Ontario. Wavy leaf margins are distinctive. The minute flowers on drooping jointed stalks have 6 sepals, of which the inner 3 enlarge to become the reddish-brown "valves". The lower central portion of each valve becomes a spongy or corky "grain".

TO 2 m

4-10dm

4-5 mm

TO 1m

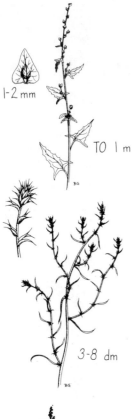

SPEARSCALE
(Atriplex patula)

The fleshy arrow-shaped leaves and the pair of arrow-shaped bracts enclosing the flower (or seed) are distinctive features of Spearscale. Like the other plants on this page, it is characteristic of open salty roadsides, where it often grows without much competition, since few Ontario plants are adapted to the high levels of de-icing salt. The plants normally reach maturity in late summer and autumn. Several varieties have been recognized on the basis of variation in the shape of their leaves and bracts.

RUSSIAN THISTLE
(Salsola kali var. *tenuifolia)*

Russian Thistle occurs throughout Ontario in dry open ground, especially along roadsides and railways, and in vacant city lots. Inconspicuous flowers are protected by short spine-tipped leaves. The lower leaves are slender and soft (3-7 cm long), but they disappear in autumn, leaving a roundish spiny bush with characteristic red or green lines on the stem. The dead plants break at the base and are blown about, gradually shattering and releasing the seeds. Another common "tumbleweed" is the Tumble Mustard (p. 131).

GOOSEFOOT
(Chenopodium album)
Pigweed, Lamb's-quarters

This close relative of garden Spinach is reported to be richer in both vitamin A and C, and it contains lots of calcium. An excellent potherb, it is best collected when young. Pigs like it, hence the name Pigweed, but this should not deter the gourmet, since, as the wild food enthusiast Euell Gibbons pointed out, pigs also like strawberry shortcake and caviar! Leaves (often fleshy) are green above and whitish-green below. Red or green lines develop on the lower stems. Goosefoot is a common and widespread weed of wastelands and cultivated ground. *Cheno* is from the Greek word for "goose"; *podium* means "foot".

(174)

REDROOT PIGWEED
(Amaranthus retroflexus)

The basal part of the stem (near the root) is usually reddish, but further up it is green and rough with dense short hair. Whitish veins protrude on the lower surface of the leaves. Stiff, needle-like bracts (4-8 mm) exceed the roundish-tipped sepals (3-4 mm). Green Amaranth (*A. powellii*) has longer, more slender inflorescence branches, longer bracts (2-3 times as long as the sepals), and the sepals are sharply pointed. Both are weeds of wasteland and cultivated ground, but Redroot Pigweed is the more common.

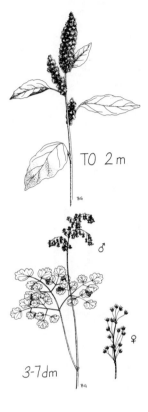

TO 2 m

EARLY MEADOW-RUE
(Thalictrum dioicum)

Early Meadow-rue, a plant of rich woodlands, blooms in April and May before its long-stalked leaves are fully expanded and before the forest canopy is well developed. Pollen is carried from male plants to female plants by the wind: the name *dioicum* refers to the two different sexes of plants. Other native Meadow-rues are taller (to 2.5 m), flower in summer, and have short-stalked leaves. Purple Meadow-rue (*T. dasycarpum*) differs from Tall Meadow-rue (*T. polygamum*) in having longer anthers (1.5-3.5 mm).

3-7 dm

BLUE COHOSH
(Caulophyllum thalictroides)

The hard blue berry-like fruits (actually naked seeds) are as attractive in July as the flowers are in April and May. Two varieties of this interesting plant may be found. One is early flowering with dark purplish foliage, deep maroon flowers, pointed sepals 6-8 mm long, and styles 1-1.7 mm long. The other blooms later, has lighter-green foliage, pale yellowish-green or pale-yellow flowers, rounded sepals 4-5 mm long, and a short style 0.2-0.6 mm long. The yellowish-green flowered variety is less common, occurring mostly in rich river bottoms and limestone forests, whereas the maroon-flowered variety has a general distribution in southern Ontario outside the Canadian Shield region.

3-8 dm

2-6 dm

GINSENG
(Panax quinquefolium)

In pioneer days the native Ginseng was much sought after for its valuable root. The early market appears to have been China, where the plant is highly esteemed as a herbal medicine. It soon became rare and it still is, although commercial production may have relieved some of the pressure on remaining natural populations. It should not be collected. The Dwarf Ginseng (*P. trifolium*), reaching 20 cm tall, is without stalked leaflets and has white flowers in May and early June. It is widespread in Ontario, and has no commercial value. (See also Wild Sarsaparilla, p. 113, which has pinnately divided leaves.)

COMMON RAGWEED
(Ambrosia artemesiifolia)

Windblown Ragweed pollen is the most important cause of hay fever in August and September. This distressing allergy is often wrongly attributed to Canada Goldenrod (p. 139), whose pollen is transported by insects. It is difficult to escape from Ragweed, but since the plant is most often encountered in wastelands and vacant lots, along roadsides and railways, and in cultivated land, the nearest deep-forested wilderness may offer relief. Drooping male flower heads in elongated raceme-like clusters produce clouds of light pollen. Female flowers, lower on the stem, produce a single seed (about 3 mm long). Note the deeply divided and basally opposite fern-like leaves.

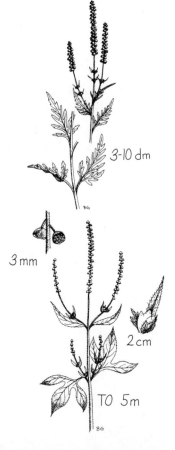

3-10 dm

3 mm

2 cm

TO 5m

GIANT RAGWEED
(Ambrosia trifida)

Giant Ragweed is characteristic of more moist and often more shaded situations than is the Common Ragweed. It occurs on flood plains, wooded slopes and stream banks, and occasionally in wasteland and cultivated fields. The leaves (to 20 cm) are 3-5 lobed and have slightly winged stalks. Like Common Ragweed, it produces large amounts of airborne pollen in late summer. It is widespread in Ontario but becomes more local northward in the Boreal Forest region.

Other Distinctive Plant Groups

Sedges

Sedges represent a large and important group in our flora. We probably have at least 300 different species in the province. They dominate some kinds of wetland plant communities and some represent an important source of food for ducks and geese. However, they are frequently overlooked. Since the pollen is carried by the wind, the flowers need not be showy like insect-pollinated blossoms. The sedge flower is composed of small scale-like bracts enclosing 2 or 3 stamens and/or an ovary with 2 or 3 style branches. Many flowers are grouped together into clusters called spikelets. The stems are usually solid and triangular in cross-section. Foliage is often arranged in 3 vertical ranks, and the sheaths (the envelopes of tissue surrounding the stem to which the leaves are attached) are closed tightly. It is not always easy to see all these characteristic features of sedges in any one plant, and there are some exceptions.

Some sedges have perfect flowers (i.e. both male and female parts in a single flower) and bristles attached at the base of the ovary. Others are without bristles and have mostly unisexual flowers. Cotton-grasses (e.g. *Eriophorum viridi-carinatum*, A) are actually sedges belonging to the former group. The numerous long silky bristles give the fruiting clusters the appearance of cotton and aid in wind dispersal of the individual seeds by increasing the surface area without adding appreciably to the weight. Several species of Cotton-grass are found in Ontario, almost always in bogs.

Sometimes the Bulrushes (e.g. *Scirpus americanus*, B) are confused with the Cat-tails (see p. 182). Bulrushes, like Cotton-grasses, have bristles at the base of the ovary and later the seed. Some species of Bulrushes develop very long bristles, giving them a cottony or woolly appearance, but they differ from Cotton-grasses in having less than 9 per seed. There are about 20 species of Bulrushes in Ontario. Some have lateral flower clusters and leaves shorter than the main stem, while others have terminal flower clusters and leafy stems. All the common species are characteristic of wetlands. Three-square Bulrush (*S. americanus*) differs from other Bulrushes in having sharply 3-angled stems, and leaves that are shorter than the main stem.

The Spike-rushes (e.g. *Eleocharis palustris*, C) include about 20 Ontario species, of which several are quite common in moist ground and along shorelines. The Spike-rushes differ from most other sedges in having a single erect terminal spikelet, in being essentially without leaves, and in having seeds with a tubercle on top.

The largest group within our sedge flora is the genus *Carex*. At least 200 species are found in Ontario. The flowers are usually unisexual, without bristles, and the fruit is enclosed in a sac-like or flask-shaped structure called a perigynium. The mature perigynia are important for the identification of many species. Most of our sedges are found in moist places. *C. intumescens*, D, is widespread in southern Ontario and the southern parts of northern Ontario, in moist woods and meadows. It is one of several species with a very inflated perigynium (i.e. much larger than the seed inside). Many species of sedges are found in deciduous and mixed woods (e.g. *C. arctata*, E). These generally grow rapidly and flower early with the other woodland herbs that take advantage of the light available before the woodland canopy is completely developed. *Carex aquatilis*, F, is one of several species of sedges that occur in marshlands and along shorelines. It is sometimes an emergent aquatic in water up to 30 cm deep.

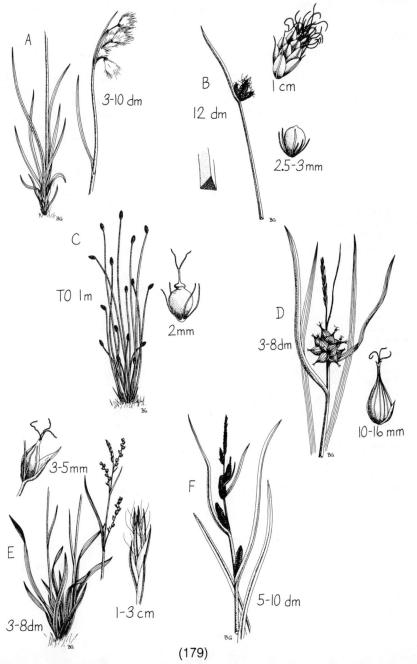

A 3-10 dm

B 12 dm 1 cm 2.5-3 mm

C TO 1 m 2mm

D 3-8dm 10-16 mm

E 3-5mm 3-8dm 1-3 cm

F 5-10 dm

(179)

Grasses

Grasses differ from sedges in having jointed circular stems with hollow internodes, and in having the sheaths at the base of the leaf blade open by a slit instead of entirely closed. In addition, grasses often have a conspicuous appendage at the base of the leaf blade, called a ligule. They are similar to sedges in having inconspicuous wind-pollinated flowers. The inner floral parts are enclosed by 2 bracts, the palea and the lemma, which together comprise a floret. Two empty bracts, called glumes, more or less enclose one or more florets. The floret(s) and the glumes are collectively referred to as a spikelet. Many spikelets are arranged in a variety of inflorescence types ranging from spikes and racemes to panicles. Grasses represent a very important part of our flora. Several habitat types are dominated by them, and about 300 species occur here without cultivation. The cultivated grasses (rice, wheat, corn) are among our most important food sources.

Kentucky Bluegrass (*Poa pratensis*, A) spreads into large patches and forms a dense sward when cut regularly, making it one of the most popular lawn grasses. It may be encountered in a great variety of habitats. The Annual Bluegrass (*P. annua*) is a low species of roadsides, lawns, and wastelands, which flowers in spring and fall. It forms light-green patches in lawns but is less desirable than *P. pratensis*, since it often dies back in midsummer. With a 10X magnifier, look for cobwebby hair at the base of the lemma in *P. pratensis*, which helps distinguish it from *P. annua*. Several other Bluegrasses occur in Ontario.

Orchard Grass (*Dactylis glomerata*, B) is a Eurasian plant now widely established in pastures, along roadsides, and in woodlands. It is an important source of fodder, but also contributes to early season hay fever. Persisting flowering stalks aid in identification.

Quack Grass (*Agropyron repens*, C) is our most common of several *Agropyron* species. It has a distinctive spike-like inflorescence with the broad side of the spikelets against the stem. The similar Rye Grass (*Lolium perenne*) has only one glume, and the narrow edge of the spikelet is against the stem.

Blue-joint (*Calamagrostis canadensis*, D) often forms pure stands in open moist ground at the edges of swamps and marshes. The hairs at the base of the lemma are like those of some Bluegrasses, but Blue-joint has only one flower per spikelet.

Timothy (*Phleum pratense*, E) is the most extensively planted hay species, usually sown in a mixture with clover or alfalfa. The cylindrical spike-like inflorescence (5-30 cm long) and the long-pointed glumes are distinctive. Also introduced from Europe and/or Asia, this species is widespread in meadows, in wastelands, and along roadsides.

Green Foxtail (*Setaria viridis*, F) is one of several Foxtails found in Ontario, all of which are introduced from Europe or Asia. The spikelets of Green Foxtail have 1 fertile floret and are about 2.5 mm long. Look for it in fields, in wastelands, along roadsides, and often in cracks in sidewalks.

Some Useful References

Moore, W. O. 1977. Some very common grasses. Michigan Botanist, 14(4): 167-188.

Dore, W. G. 1959. Grasses of the Ottawa District. Research Branch, Canada Dept. of Agriculture. Publ. 1049. 73 pp.+ appendices.

Dore, W. G. and J. McNeill. 1978. Grasses of Ontario. Agriculture Canada, Ottawa. (in press)

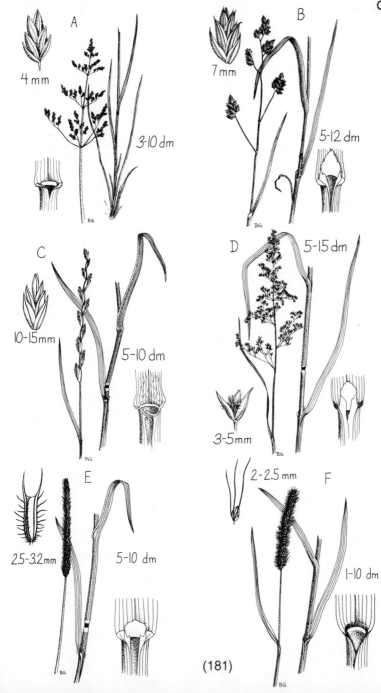

A — 4 mm — 3-10 dm

B — 7 mm — 5-12 dm

C — 10-15 mm — 5-10 dm

D — 5-15 dm — 3-5 mm

E — 2.5-3.2 mm — 5-10 dm

F — 2-2.5 mm — 1-10 dm

(181)

Grass-leaved Plants

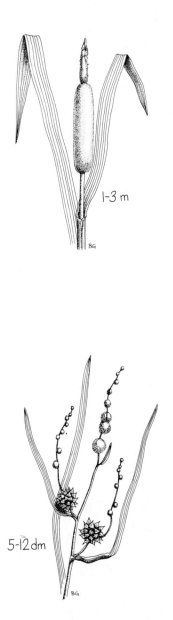

1-3 m

BG

5-12 dm

BG

COMMON CAT-TAIL
(*Typha latifolia*)

Everyone has seen Cat-tail marshes, and most children have battled with the stiff dry fruiting stalks which remain erect all winter. The velvety-brown flower spikes are most attractive in a dry bouquet but must be collected early, otherwise they will disintegrate into a mass of fluffy seeds, 147 000—220 000 per spike. It is reported that one seed can give rise to 100 shoots and a root system 3 m across in a single growing season. The male (pollen-producing) flowers form a narrow spike above the female flowers. In Common Cat-tail, the male and female portions of the spike are adjacent to one another, but in the Narrow-leaved Cat-tail (*T. angustifolia*), they are separated by a section of stem without any flowers. The leaves of Common Cat-tail are 6-15 mm wide, while those of Narrow-leaved Cat-tail range from 3-8 mm. Many of the Cat-tails we find are neither the Narrow-leaved nor the Common, but a hybrid (*T. × glauca*). Although the hybrid is intermediate in most respects, it may grow taller than either of its parents. Very young Cat-tail shoots may be used in salads, while the older (flower bud) shoots may be eaten as a cooked vegetable. Cat-tail pollen is carried from the male to the female flowers by the wind. This is more of a hit and miss process than insect pollination, and a lot of pollen is produced to ensure that some will reach its destination. Pollen is produced in sufficient abundance that it can be collected for making pancakes and muffins. The starchy roots yield a flour for bread and biscuits (see p. 194).

BUR-REED
(*Sparganium eurycarpum*)

Found in wet soil and shallow water along shorelines throughout much of Ontario, this is the most common of our several species of Bur-reeds. It may be distinguished from the others by its relatively larger seeds, 5-8 mm wide, which mature in late July and August. The flowers form dense clusters, the upper being male and the lower female. The female flowers of this species have 2 stigmas, whereas other Ontario Bur-reeds have only one. Leaves range from 6-12 mm in width.

(182)

Aquatic Plants

An aquatic plant is one which begins its growth in the water and grows at least partially submerged for much of its life. Aquatic plants may be free-floating, submerged, submerged with floating leaves, or emergent. Woody plants are generally not included since they thrive in merely moist or stranded conditions, although some such as Buttonbush, Leatherleaf, Sweet Gale, Willows, and Red Maple may often be observed in standing water. Some aquatic plants with showy flowers are treated elsewhere in this book, but many are most often found without flowers and others have small inconspicuous flowers. Some of these are illustrated in the following pages. Several guides are available which treat the group of aquatic plants in detail. Three of those in general use are listed below.

Unlike vacant lots and old fields, aquatic habitats are usually dominated by native species, but several introduced species occur especially in extreme southern Ontario. Many of our aquatic plangs (e.g. Marsh Marigold, Water-lily, Water Plantain) belong to the more primitive plant families, but a few species in the more advanced plant families have also become adapted to the aquatic environment.

The pollination of aquatic plants is a fascinating subject. Some species produce insect- or wind-pollinated flowers at the surface; others utilize the water for transfer of pollen (see Tapegrass and Coontail). The seeds of some species float (e.g. Irises and Sedges), while many others stick by surface tension to waterfowl and are distributed over great distances.

Some aquatic plants have 2 kinds of leaves. The lower submerged leaves are much dissected and thread-like, while the higher emergent or floating leaves are often roundish and more or less undivided. The submerged leaves are often thinner and have a thin outer layer to facilitate gas exchange which is much slower in water than in air. Many emergent aquatics have internal air spaces to aid in aeration.

Aquatic plants may be found in a variety of habitats, ranging from cool fast-flowing streams to warm stagnant pools. Important environmental factors include availability of organic and inorganic nutrients and dissolved gases, the penetration of light, the temperature, the nature of the substrate, and physical disturbances. In some habitats, fluctuating water levels are important to the maintenance of aquatic plant communities.

Occasionally aquatic plants are a nuisance, since they clog channels and thus prevent the passage of boats; they may also remove oxygen and increase carbon dioxide, thereby creating an unfavourable environment for sport fish. However, such aquatic plant problems are often the result of increased nutrients caused by pollution or some other human factor such as unnatural manipulation of water levels. If the problem can be traced back to the ultimate cause, sometimes much can be saved on cutting and undesirable herbicide spraying programmes. Aquatic vascular plants, in Ontario at least, are more beneficial than injurious, since they provide a necessary habitat for many sport fish, as well as food and cover for waterfowl.

Some Useful References

Muenscher, W. C. 1944. Aquatic plants of the United States. Cornell University Press. Ithaca, New York. 274 pp.

Fassett, N. C. 1957. A manual of aquatic plants. University of Wisconsin Press. Madison, Wisconsin. 405 pp.

Hotchkiss, N. 1972. Common marsh, underwater and floating-leaved plants of the United States and Canada. Dover Publications, New York. 1-99, 1-124.

COMMON WATERWEED
(Anacharis canadensis)

Common Waterweed has leaves about 1 cm long and 1.5-4 mm wide in groups of 3. The flowers, appearing in July and August, have white petals 2-3 mm (female) or to 5 mm (male). Pollen is released onto the surface of the water, where it may float to the female flowers. Common Waterweed may be found in quiet water throughout much of Ontario. Related species have either wider or narrower leaves. A South American species sold with tropical fish has 4-6 leaves in a whorl.

2-4 mm

DUCKWEED
(Lemna minor)

Take a handful of the green mat floating on a surface of still water and you may be holding hundreds of these tiny plants. *L. minor*, 2-5 mm long, with a single root is the most common, but often 2 or 3 species of the Duckweed family are found together. The "leaves" of the Star-duckweed (*L. trisulca*), 6-10 mm long, are often joined in the shape of a cross and are usually submerged. The roundish Water-flaxseed (*Spirodela polyrhiza*), 3-8 mm across, has more than one root. Little more than 1 mm in length and without roots, the Water-meals (*Wolffia* spp.) are our smallest flowering plants. In Ontario they are confined to the south, whereas the other members of the Duckweed family extend farther north. Vegetative reproduction is common in the Duckweed family, and whole plants are effectively dispersed by adhering to waterfowl.

COONTAIL
(Ceratophyllum demersum)

Leaves 1-2 cm long are irregularly divided into thread-like segments, which in *C. demersum* are toothed and forked. The axillary flowers are inconspicuous. Stamens become detached below the water and float to the surface, where they open to release the pollen. The anthers may be transported some distance over the surface, but free pollen is slightly heavier than water and gradually sinks to the submerged female flowers.

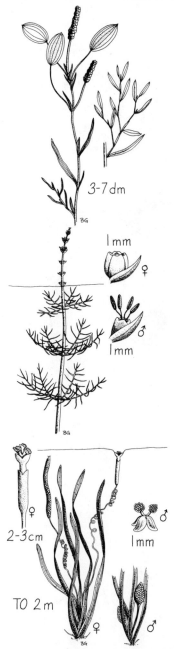

GRASSY PONDWEED
(Potamogeton gramineus)

The Pondweeds are the largest group of truly aquatic seed-plants in our region. Flowers and fruits are crowded into submerged or emergent spikes one to several centimetres in length. There are several common species in Ontario. Some, like *P. gramineus*, have elliptical floating leaves and narrow or linear submerged leaves, while others have only submerged leaves. Grassy Pondweed occurs in quiet water throughout Ontario. Its submerged leaves, 3-8 cm long, have 3-7 veins.

PALE WATER-MILFOIL
(Myriophyllum spicatum var. exalbescens)

The Water-milfoils have distinctive feathery leaves that are divided into thread-like segments. Some species have the leaves in whorls, while in others they are alternate. The small flowers with petals a few mm in length are usually borne above the water, in the axils of upper bract-like leaves. Many other aquatics are superficially similar but do not have pinnately divided leaves or leaf segments that are secondarily divided and/or have bladders (p. 139). Pale Water-milfoil is found in quiet water, 1-4 m deep, throughout much of Ontario.

TAPEGRASS
(Vallisneria americana)

The parallel veins are densely packed toward the centre of the leaf with vein-free areas along the leaf margins. Leaves are 0.5-2 cm wide. Flowering usually occurs in late July and August. Numerous male flowers become detached under water, and with air bubbles imprisoned in their sepals they rise to the surface where they float. The much larger female flowers, 2-3 cm long and about 5 mm wide, remain attached but are on long stalks. Their sepals and stigmas project above the surface. The sepals of the free-floating male flowers part when they reach the surface, acting as tiny pontoons. Water currents and gentle breezes waft the minute pollen-bearing craft to the female flower. Tapegrass occurs throughout much of Ontario, usually in quiet water.

8-15 cm

3-6 dm

1-3 dm

Arums

In the Arums, many minute flowers lacking petals are packed closely together on a fleshy stalk called a spadix and usually surrounded by a large showy bract called the spathe. "Arum" comes from the Arabian word *ar*, meaning fire, and refers to the fact that when eaten, crystals in the roots and leaves of the Arums can lodge in the throat and cause severe pain and a burning sensation.

By mid-March, Skunk Cabbage (*Symplocarpus foetidus*), is already blooming through the snow. The short yellow spadix can produce heat and raises the temperature inside the thick mottled reddish-brown and yellow spathe so that the surrounding snow is melted. At flowering time the leaves are tightly coiled beside the spathe, but by midsummer they have unfolded to full size. A strong skunky odour is produced if any of the plant tissue is broken. Skunk Cabbage is most common in swampy wet places in the Carolinian zone. Scattered records north to L. Superior may reflect a more extensive distribution in Ontario at a time when the climate was warmer than it is today.

Jack-in-the-pulpit (*Arisaema triphyllum*) is a common sight in moist rich woods and thickets in the spring. The leaves look like those of Poison Ivy except that the 3 leaflets are stalkless and their veins are joined along the margin. This plant occurs throughout the Carolinian and Mixed Forest region. In autumn, bright clusters (3-6 cm long) of red berries are produced. Confined to damp woods in the Carolinian zone, the Green Dragon (*A. dracontium*) has a long tapering green spadix, projecting up to 10 cm beyond the slender green spathe. Its single leaf is irregularly divided into 5-17 leaflets.

Flowering in summer when its heart-shaped leaves are fully expanded, the white spathe of Wild Calla (*Calla palustris*) clasps the short thick yellowish spadix only at the base. Bright red berries develop by late summer. The species name *palustris* refers to the marshy habitat of this plant, which often grows in up to 30 cm of water. Wild Calla occurs mainly in the Mixed and Boreal Forest regions.

(186)

Saprophytes and Parasites

Certain non-green plants absorb food from other living or decomposing plant material. Parasites sometimes kill their living host in the process of deriving nourishment. Saprophytes use the nutrients present in decomposing organic material.

Waxy white and semi-translucent Indian Pipes (*Monotropa uniflora*) emerge from the floor of rich dark woods, their roots absorbing nutrients from the decomposing litter. The single flower hangs from a bent stalk in summer, but as the fruiting capsule matures it turns upward. The leaves are reduced to fleshy scales. Indian Pipe is found from the Carolinian to the Boreal Forest region.

Spotted Coral-root (*Corallorhiza maculata*) is a saprophytic orchid of mixed or coniferous woodlands. A number of different forms have stems varying from yellow to reddish purple to brown, and may be found in flower from midsummer to fall. The white lip of the flower may be spotted with red, lined with red, or completely plain, but always has 3 lobes, the central one being the largest. The attractive red-and-white candy-cane striping of the Striped Coral-root (*C. striata*) is apparent in late May and June in dry cedar woods especially near limestone. Early Coral-root (*C. trifida*) has yellow stems, and flowers with a white or spotted unlobed lip. It blooms from early May to July in swamps and bogs.

Usually associated with Beech trees in the Deciduous and Mixed Forest regions, the brownish parasitic Beech-drops (*Epifagus virginiana*), blooms in late summer and autumn. Food is apparently absorbed from the roots of the Beech trees. Its branched flowering stems have a few scale-like leaves and many stalkless flowers. The upper tubular flowers, about 1 cm long, are sterile, while the lower ones produce seeds.

Masses of thread-like orange stems twining around Jewel-weed plants readily identify an infestation of the parasitic Dodder (*Cuscuta gronovii*, not illustrated). Tiny root-like projections enter the stem of the host to tap its nutrient supply.

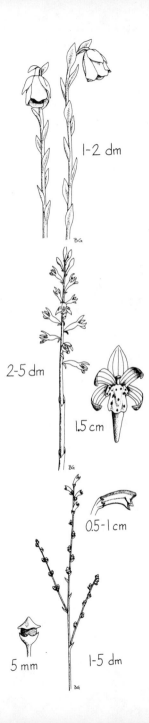

(187)

Appendix

Ferns and Fern Allies

Ferns and fern allies belong to a major group in the plant kingdom. They are distinguished from the flowering plants in being spread about in the form of spores rather than seeds. These spores give rise to an independent or free-living sexual stage called the gametophyte. In flowering plants this phase is much reduced, relatively short-lived, and occurs within the flowers. Included in the fern allies are the Club-mosses and Horsetails, which are discussed here, but also the Quillworts (slender aquatic plants) and Spike-mosses (tiny moss-like plants). During the Carboniferous Age these plants sometimes reached tree proportions, forming lush forests, but today they are relatively small, rarely exceeding 1 m in height.

Club-mosses are low evergreens with small (about 1 cm or less) "leaves" encircling the stem. Seven species occur in Ontario, mostly in the Canadian Shield region and less commonly southward. Shining Club-moss (*Lycopodium lucidulum*, A) creeps over the ground, curving up at the tip where the stem forks once or twice. Spores are borne at the base of short non-toothed leaves, 4-8 mm, in zones between longer sterile leaves, 6-12 mm long. Ground Pine (*L. obscurum*, B) has leaves that are shiny dark-green and narrowly pointed. Ground Cedar (*L. complanatum*) has flattened leaves which produce branches that look similar to those of White Cedar, but has a habit of growth similar to Ground Pine.

Horsetails have jointed stems with small, often papery, teeth (the leaves) at each joint. Ridges along the stem are roughened with silica, and the tiny green spores are borne in terminal cone-like structures. The Field Horsetail (*Equisetum arvense*, C) grows in a variety of habitats from swamps to sand dunes and woodlands. It differs from most other Horsetails in having 2 kinds of stems: pale-brown unbranched spore-producing stems that appear in early spring, and green branched stems that are produced a few weeks later when the cone-bearing stems have withered. The Meadow Horsetail (*E. pratense*) is similar, but the cones are produced on branching green stems. The secondary branching whorls of the Woodland Horsetail (*E. sylvaticum*, D) give it a most attractive feathery appearance. The main stems have loose sheaths with broad brown teeth grouped in 2s or 3s. Woodland Horsetail is found in moist open woods and swamps in the Mixed and Boreal Forest regions.

Common Scouring Rush (*E. hyemale*, E) is one of a group of unbranched Horsetails that produce various hybrids difficult to identify. The stems of Scouring Rush are thick, firm, and evergreen, and have 12-50 ridges. Dense stands are often found along sandy shores and at the base of moist slopes. Smooth Scouring Rush (*E. laevigatum*) with softer non-evergreen stems and somewhat longer stem sheaths (10-16 mm), is less common. Variegated Scouring Rush (*E. variegatum*), a smaller plant with stiff narrow evergreen stems, has 6-12 stem ridges.

Rattlesnake Fern (*Botrychium virginianum*, F) is one of the several members of the Grape Ferns occurring in Ontario. Other less common species have either more or less dissected leaves, but all have the characteristic spore-bearing "clusters of grapes", and in Rattlesnake Fern the individual branches look like the end of a rattlesnake's tail. The single yellowish-green leaf, which appears in spring, is 3-parted and much divided. This fern occurs in the humus of rich Mixed and Deciduous woods throughout Ontario.

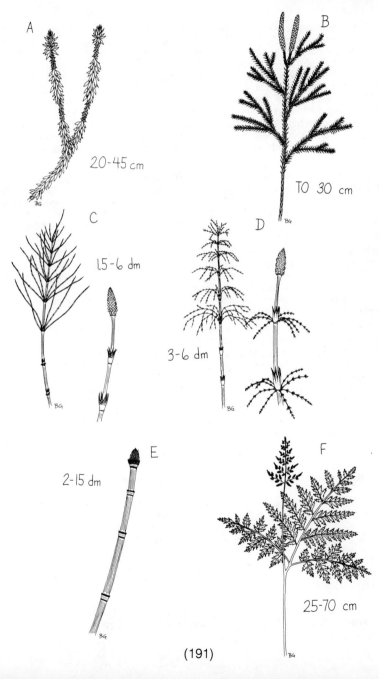

A 20-45 cm

B TO 30 cm

C 1.5-6 dm

D 3-6 dm

E 2-15 dm

F 25-70 cm

Those highly esteemed vegetable greens called fiddleheads come from the Ostrich Fern (*Matteuccia struthiopteris*, A). The fiddleheads are actually the young green leaves, which are curled into tight coils. They may be collected from late April to early June when they are about 20 cm tall. Only one fiddlehead should be collected per plant since the removal of these young leaves weakens the plants. Fiddleheads of other fern species are small or bitter, and some may even be poisonous. The Ostrich Fern can be distinguished by its brownish plume-like fertile fronds (leaves). These spore-producing structures are much shorter than the green sterile fronds, which reach 1 m. In addition, the fertile fronds are stiff and durable and persist all winter into the following spring. Ostrich Fern occurs throughout much of southern Ontario, extending north into the southern Boreal Forest region. It is characteristic of moist woods and is especially prevalent in periodically flooded bottom-land forests.

Sensitive Fern (*Onoclea sensibilis*, B) also has dimorphic (2 kinds of) fronds, but they are much shorter and have fewer lobes than those of Ostrich Fern. Forms with semi-dimorphic fronds (*f. obtusiloba*) are sometimes found. The leaf stalks arise from a creeping rootstock Pale-green sterile fronds are 12-30 cm long, and are sensitive to the early autumn frosts, hence the common name. Sensitive Fern occurs in wet meadows and moist woods throughout much of Ontario.

The Bracken Fern (*Pteridium aquilinum*, C) is a plant of relatively dry acid sites in full sun or partial shade. The large deltoid leaves (30-70 cm long) on stalks up to 100 cm arise singly from a horizontal underground rhizome. Spores are produced on the underside of the leaf in the inrolled leaf margins. The foliage is reported to make cattle sick and to produce cancer in laboratory rats. It should not be used as a wild-food source until its effects on humans have been studied in more detail.

In swamplands and about streams in woodlands and especially in rocky woods, one may find a variety of ferns, but four species are particularly common and distributed over much of the province. The Lady Fern (*Athyrium felix-femina*, D) has delicate fronds (to 90 cm) with curved or comma-shaped sori (spore-dots) on the underside. Spinulose Wood Fern (*Dryopteris spinulosa*, E) has a tougher frond, which occasionally remains green all winter, and the sori on the underside are circular. The similar Evergreen Wood Fern (*D. intermedia*) is almost always evergreen and has longer, less triangular, and less ascending primary leaf segments. Marginal Wood Fern (*D. marginalis*, F) has dark bluish-green fronds and differs from the preceding Wood Ferns in having the circular sori on the margins or edges of the frond segments. It is also evergreen.

Some Useful References

Britton, D. M. 1969. Ferns of the Bruce Trail. Ontario Naturalist 7(2): 13-19.

Brunton, D. F. and J. D. Lafontaine. 1973-4. Fern allies of the Ottawa-Hull District. Trail and Landscape 7(4): 90-95. 8(1): 18-23. 8(2): 46-49.

Cody, W. J. 1956. Ferns of the Ottawa District. Canada Dept. of Agriculture. Ottawa. Publ. 974. 94 pp.

Reznicek, T. A. 1972. The ferns of Simcoe County, Ontario. Brereton Field Naturalists Club, Barrie, Ontario. 10 pp.

Wherry, E. T. 1961. The fern guide—northeastern and midland United States and adjacent Canada. Doubleday & Co., Garden City, New York. 318 pp.

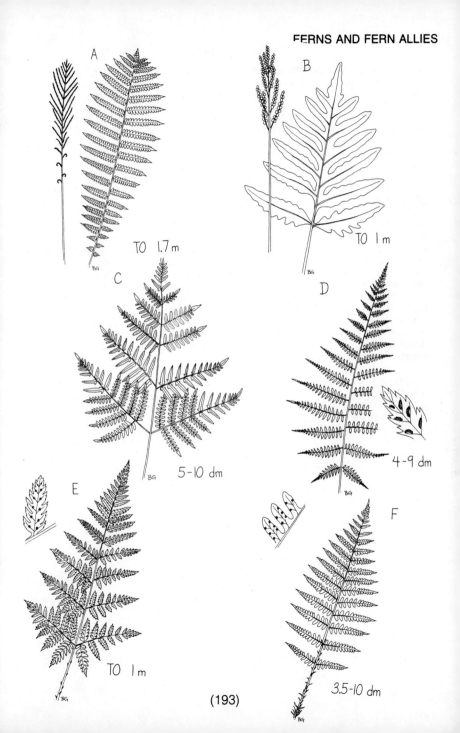

A

TO 1.7 m

B

TO 1 m

C

5-10 dm

D

4-9 dm

E

TO 1 m

F

3.5-10 dm

(193)

Edible Plants

Over the past several years there has been a tremendous increase in the use of wild plants for food and health purposes, a use that has had an unfortunate effect on our native flora. Some species are becoming rare wherever there are people. The ability of a plant species to withstand heavy collecting pressure depends upon the lifespan of the plant and the part of the plant collected. Harvesting the berries from our native berry bushes, and the nuts from Hickories, Oaks, and Walnuts, may reduce their ability to reproduce, but does not kill the plant. Collecting the roots or tubers of native wildflowers, however, does destroy the entire plant. If the plant is already uncommon or restricted to a patchy habitat (*e.g.* woodlands in southern Ontario), excessive collecting sometimes results in local extinction. Some books concerning the use of wild plants for food fail to make any distinction between uncommon native species and common weeds, and most fail to mention the significance of the part that is collected. After numerous people have come to dig the Wild Onions and Spring Beauty, and gather the Violets, a spring woodland is transformed from a beautiful natural garden to a trampled mess. With the exception of the various nuts and berries and some of the more common native species, such as Cat-tails and Common Milkweed, one should not collect native plants. It is also important to remember that wildlife is dependent upon some of these natural food resources whereas we are not. Some native plants could be gathered with discretion in areas where they are especially abundant. Among these are plants such as Jewel-weed, Field Mint, Pokeweed, Ground Nut, Sassafras, and Wintergreen. We would discourage the use of all Violets, since some are so difficult to identify that very rare species are sometimes collected. Natural strains of Ginseng are already uncommon to rare. Other native species commonly used for food such as Pawpaw and Cherry Birch are common to the south of us, but are not common enough in Ontario to justify their use as wild foods. Water-lilies and Arrowhead are important components of the aquatic ecosystem and should therefore not be collected.

However there is no reason why a conservation-minded individual should not eat wild plants! A great variety of introduced, aggressive and weedy plants are available. There is really no need to gather uncommon native species. Have you tried Coltsfoot (p. 143) as a cure for coughs and colds? What about Chicory (p. 171) or Dandelion (p. 144) tea? Do sliced Burdock (p. 160) roots really increase strength, endurance, and vitality? Day-lily (p. 145) soup may be more to your taste. Pigweed (p. 174) is an excellent potherb, and it is hard not to find! Some other common introduced plants that can be used for food or health purposes are (from top to bottom of page): 1 on p. 46, 1 on p. 102, 2 on p. 103, 2 on p. 109, 1 on p. 116, 2 on p. 121, 3 on p. 125, 1 on p. 129, 1 & 2 on p. 132, 1 on p. 138, 2 on p. 144, 1 on p. 145, 1 on p. 162, 3 on p. 166, 3 on p. 171, 1 & 3 on p. 173, 1 on p. 174 and 1 on p. 175. Recipes for some or all of these can be found in the selection of references below.

References

Angier, B. 1972. Feasting free on wild edibles. Stackpole Books, Harrisburg, Pa. 313 pp.

Fernald, M. L. and A. C. Kinsey. (Revised by R. C. Rollins). 1958. Edible wild plants of eastern North America. Harper and Row Publ. New York. 452 pp.

Gibbons, E. 1962. Stalking the wild asparagus. David McKay Co. New York. 303 pp.

Gibbons, E. 1966. Stalking the healthful herbs. David McKay Co. New York. 303 pp.

Poisonous Plants

What is meant by the word "poisonous"? Generally we think of poisonous plants as those that cause physiological disorder or death, but often plants that cause allergies are also included in the definition. Where do we come in contact with poisonous plants? They are everywhere. Some city dwellers actually believe that poisonous plants are found only in the countryside or the remote wilderness, but most cases of serious child poisonings by plants in our area are a result of poisonous houseplants such as Oleander, Ivy, Azalea, Pencil Tree, Dumb Cane and Philodendron. Dumb Cane causes swelling of the throat and tongue and sometimes death by suffocation while a little Oleander foliage can cause death by paralysis. It is surprising in some respects to see these house-plants for sale in the supermarket not far from the cereals and vegetables. Of course adults know enough not to eat them but young children explore with their sense of taste. Garden ornamentals including Thorn Apple, Larkspur, Daffodil, and Castor Bean are also toxic, the latter especially so in the form of a seed necklace. The Mistletoe, Holly and Jerusalem Cherry are also poisonous if eaten.

A variety of wild plants are poisonous, and "living off the land" can be dangerous. Poison Hemlock and Water Hemlock have been mistaken for Wild Parsley, and Moonseed for Wild Grape. Plants in this book that produce more or less poisonous berries (or fruits) are (from top to bottom of page): 1 on p. 25, 3 on p. 54, 1 on p. 66, 2 on p. 78, both on p. 79, 1 on p. 82, 1 & 3 on . 91, 1 on p. 94, 1 on p. 95, 3 on p. 96, 3 on p. 98, all on p. 100, 3 on p. 104, 3 on p. 105, 1 on p. 107, 2 on p. 122, 3 on p. 127, 1 on p. 128, 3 on p. 150, 3 on p. 175, and all on p. 186. Plants with more or less poisonous foliage (in addition to some of the above) include: 1 on p. 49, 3 on p. 104, 3 on p. 107, 3 on p. 114, 1 & 3 on p. 115, 1 on p. 123, 3 on p. 129, 3 on p. 130, 2 on p. 136, and 1 on p. 173. Sometimes not all parts of an edible plant are edible. Just as a green potato or the leaves of Rhubarb are poisonous, the berries or mature leaves of Pokeweed are poisonous although the young sprouts are a delicacy. The immature fruits of May-apple should also be avoided along with the cyanide-containing stones of Black Cherry. Sometimes the name of a plant suggests edibility, when in fact the plant is poisonous. Examples are the mildly poisonous grain-like tubers of the Squirrel Corn (p. 108) and the young fruits of May-apple (p. 107).

Allergic responses are caused by physical contact. Skin irritation may result from hypodermic injection (e.g. Stinging Nettle, p. 173) or contact with sap (e.g. Poison Ivy, p. 94). The airborne pollen of various trees, grasses, and Ragweed causes respiratory allergies; Goldenrods and Dandelions, however, do not.

Just because poisonous plants are around us does not mean that an eradication program is needed. Some of our native poisonous plants, including Poison Ivy, represent important food and cover for wildlife. Except for hay fever, most of the difficulties arise through carelessness and ignorance. Be aware of the dangers, protect children, and handle the plants with care.

References

Arnold Arboretum. 1974. Poisonous plants. (Reprint of) Arnoldia 34(2): 41-96. (Harvard University, Jamaica Plain, Massachusetts).

Hardin, J. W. and J. M. Arena. 1973. Human poisoning from native and cultivated plants. Duke University Press, Durham, North Carolina. 167 pp. (2nd ed.)

Montgomery, F. H. Poisonous fruits. Special Publ. #1, Federation of Ontario Naturalists. Don Mills, Ontario. 24 pp.

INDEX

Abies balsamea, 26
Abutilon theophrastis, 155
Acer spp., 50, 51, 64
Achillea millefolium, 125, 194
Actaea spp., 105, 195
Adder's Tongue, Yellow, 127
Agrimonia spp., 134
Agrimony, 134
Agropyron repens, 180
Ailanthus altissima, 49
Alder, Black, 79, 195
    Green, 55
    Speckled, 55
Alfalfa, 162, 194
Alisma plantago-aquatica, 99
Alliaria officinalis, 108
Allium tricoccum, 99
Alnus spp., 55
Amaranth, Green, 175
Amaranthus spp., 175, 194
Ambrosia spp., 176, 195
Amelanchier spp., 62
Amphicarpa bracteata, 98
Anacharis canadensis, 184
Anaphilis margaritacea, 125
Andromeda glaucophylla, 87
Anemone, Canada, 106
    Long-headed, 106
    Wood, 106
Anemone spp., 106
Angel's-trumpet, 120
Antennaria spp., 125
Anthemis cotula, 126
Apios americana, 98
Apocynum spp., 156
Apple, May-, 107, 195
    Thorn, 120
    Wild Crab, 43
Aquilegia canadensis, 148
Aralia spp., 113
Arbutus, Trailing, 161
Arctium spp., 160
Arctostaphylos uva-ursi, 83
Arisaema spp., 186, 195
Aronia spp., 75
Arrowhead, Broad-leaved, 99

Arrow-wood, Downy, 90
    Southern, 90
Artichoke, Jerusalem, 142
Asarum canadense, 147
Asclepias spp., 157
Ash, American Mountain-, 60
    Black, 52
    Blue, 52
    European Mountain-, 60
    Green, 53
    Prickly, 69
    Red, 53
    Showly Mountain-, 60
    White, 53
Asimina triloba, 58
Asparagus officinalis, 102, 194
Asparagus, Wild, 102, 194
Aspen, Large-toothed, 32
    Trembling, 32
Aster, Amethyst, 123
    Bog, 170
    Calico, 124
    Flat-topped White, 124
    Heart-leaved, 169
    Heath, 123
    Large-leaved, 170
    New England, 170
    Smooth, 169
    Swamp, 171
Aster cordifolius, 169
    ericoides, 123
    laevis, 169
    lateriflorus, 124
    macrophyllus, 170
    nemoralis, 170
    novae-angliae, 170
    puniceus, 171
    umbellatus, 124
Athyrium filix-femina, 192
Atriplex patula, 174, 194
Avens, Yellow, 134

Balsam Fir, 26
Baneberry, Red, 105
    White, 105, 195
Barbarea vulgaris, 132, 194

Barberry, Common, 72
       Japanese, 72
Basswood, American, 38
Bastard Toadflax, 117
Beach Pea, 153
Bearberry, 83
Beard-tongue, Hairy, 158
Bedstraw, Fragrant, 122
       Northern, 122
Beebalm, Scarlet, 157
Beech, American, 39, 187
      Blue, or Muscle, 59
Beech-drops, 187
Beggar's-ticks, 143
Bellflower, Creeping, 168
Bellwort, Large-flowered, 127
      Sessile, 127
Berberis spp., 72
Bergamot, Wild, 157
Berry, Buffalo-, 83
    Wolf, 92
Betula spp., 37, 69
Bidens cernua, 142
    frondosa, 143
Bilberries, 84
Bindweed, Black, 102
      Field, 119
      Hedge, 119
Birch, Cherry, 37
    Grey, 37
    Swamp, 69
    White, 37
    Yellow, 37
Bird's-foot Trefoil, 135
Bitter-cress, 152
Bittersweet, Climbing, 95, 195
    -Nightshade, 98
Blackberries, 77
Black-eyed Susan, 142
Black Gum, 47
Bladdernut, 72
Bladderworts, 139
Blazing Star, 159
Bloodroot, 107, 195
Bluebead-lily, 127, 195
Bluebell, Northern, 165
      Round-leaved, 168
      Virginia, 165

Blueberry, Dry-land, 84
      Highbush, 84
      Low Sweet, 84
      Velvet-leaf, 85
Blue Cohosh, 175
Blue-eyed Grass, Common, 163
       Slender, 163
Blue Flag, 162
Bluegrass, Annual, 180
      Kentucky, 180
Blue-joint, 180
Blue Vervain, 166
Blueweed, 165
Boehmeria cylindrica, 173
Bog-laurel, 87
Bog-rosemary, 87
Boneset, 122
Botrychium virginianum, 190
Bower, Virgin's, 95
Bracken Fern, 192
Brambles, 76
Brassica spp., 132
Brooklime, American, 168
Buckbean, 119
Buckthorn, Alder-leaved, 66
      Common, 66, 195
      Glossy, 66
Buckwheat, 102
Buffalo-berry, 83
Bugloss, Viper's, 165
Bulrush, Three-square, 178
Bunchberry, 118
Bur Cucumber, 97
Burdock, Common, 160, 194
      Great, 160
Bur-marigold, 142
Burning Bush, 82
Bur-reed, 182
Butter and Eggs, 138
Buttercups, 130
Butternut, 35
Butterprint, 155
Buttonbush, 83

Cabbage, Skunk, 186, 195
Calamagrostis canadensis, 180
Calla palustris, 186, 195
Calla, Wild, 186, 195

INDEX

Calopogon tuberosus, 151
Caltha palustris, 129, 195
Campanula spp., 168
Campion, Bladder, 104
Canada Anemone, 106
Canada Mayflower, 100, 195
Canada Moonseed, 96, 195
Canada Plum, 61
Canada Violet, 112
Cannabis sativa, 172
Capsella bursa-pastoris, 109, 194
Caragana arborescens, 78
Cardamine spp., 152
Cardinal Flower, 149
Carduus nutans, 160
Carex spp., 178
Carpinus caroliniana, 59
Carrot, Wild, 116, 194
Carrion-flower, 96
Carya spp., 36
Cassandra, 86
Castanea dentata, 39
Castilleja coccinea, 149
Catchfly, Night-flowering, 104
Catchfly, Sleepy, 104
Catnip, 166, 194
Cat-tail, Common, 181, 194
    Narrow-leaved, 182
Caulophyllum thalictroides, 175, 195
Ceanothus spp., 82
Cedar, Eastern Red, 25
    Eastern White, 27
    Ground, 190
Celastris scandens, 95, 195
Celandine, 130, 195
Celtis spp., 43
Cephalanthus occidentalis, 83
Cerastium spp., 103
Ceratophyllum demersum, 184
Chamaedaphne calyculata, 86
Cheeses, 155
Chelidonium majus, 130, 195
Chelone glabra, 121
Chenopodium album, 174
Cherry, Black, 49, 195
    Choke, 61
    Pin, 61
    Sand, 61

Chestnut, Sweet, 39
Chickweed, Common, 103, 194
            Common Mouse-ear, 103
            Field, 103
Chicory, 171, 194
Chimaphila umbellata, 117
Chokeberries, 75
Chrysanthemum leucanthemum, 126
Cicely, Sweet, 114
Cichorium intybus, 171
Cicuta spp., 115, 195
Cinquefoil, Marsh, 149
            Rough, 133
            Shrubby, 92
            Sulphur, 133
Circaea spp., 113
Cirsium arvense, 160
        muticum, 160
        vulgare, 161
Claytonia spp., 103
Cleavers, 122
Clematis, Purple, 95
Clematis spp., 95
Clintonia borealis, 127, 195
Cloudberry, 77
Clover, Alsike, 153
        Red, 153
        White, 112
        White Sweet, 112
        Yellow Sweet, 135
Club-moss, Shining, 190
Cockle, White, 104
Cockspur-thorn, 63
Coffee-tree, Kentucky, 54
Cohosh, Blue, 175, 195
Coltsfoot, 143, 194
Columbine, Wild, 148
Comandra umbellata, 117
Conium maculatum, 114, 195
Coontail, 184
Convolvulus spp., 119
Conyza canadensis, 124
Coptis trifolia, 105
Corallorhiza spp., 187
Coral-root, Early, 187
            Spotted, 187
            Striped, 187
Corn, Squirrel, 108, 195

Cornus alternifolia, 65
    amomum, 80
    canadensis, 118
    drummondii, 80
    florida, 65
    obliqua, 80
    purpusi, 80
    racemosa, 80
    rugosa, 81
    stolonifera, 81
Corydalis spp., 152
Corydalis, Golden, 152
    Pink, 152
Corylus spp., 68
Cotton-grass, 178
Cottonwood, Eastern, 32
Cow Parsnip, 115
Crab Apple, Wild, 43
Crampbark, 89
Cranberry, Highbush, 89
    Large Bog, 85
    Mountain, 85
    Small Bog, 85
Crataegus spp., 63
Creeper, Virginia, 95
Cress, Bitter-, 152
    Spring-, 152
    Winter, 132, 194
Crinkleroot, 109
Cucumber, Bur, 97
    Wild, 97
Cucumber-root, Indian, 128
Cucumber Tree, 47
Currant, Black, 71
    Bristly Black, 70
    Red, 70
    Skunk, 70
    Wild Black, 71
    Wild Red, 70
Cuscuta gronovii, 187
Cypripedium acaule, 151
    calceolus, 128
    reginae, 151

Dactylis glomerata, 180
Daisy, Ox-eye, 126
Dame's Rocket, 109

Dandelion, Common, 144, 194
    Red-seeded, 144
Datura stramonium, 120
Daucus carota, 116, 194
Day-lily, Orange, 145, 194
Deerberry, 84
Dentaria ssp., 109
Deptford Pink, 148
Desmodium canadense, 153
Dewberry, 77
Dianthus armeria, 148
Dicentra spp., 108, 195
Diervilla lonicera, 92
Diplotaxis spp., 131
Dipsacus sylvestris, 159
Dirca palustris, 82
Dock, Curly, 173, 194
Dodder, 187
Dogbane, Spreading, 156
Dog-tooth Violet, 127
Dogwood, Alternate-leaved, 65
    Eastern Flowering, 65
    Grey, 80
    Red Osier, 81
    Rough-leaved, 80
    Round-leaved, 81
    Silky, 80
Drosera spp., 110
Dryopteris spp., 192
Duckweed, 184
    Star-, 184
Dutchman's Breeches, 108

Echinocystis lobata, 97
Echium vulgare, 165
Elder, Common, 91
    Red-berried, 91, 195
Elecampane, 141
Eleocharis palustris, 178
Elephant's-ear, 155
Elms, 44
Enchanter's Nightshade, 113
Epifagus virginiana, 187
Epigaea repens, 161
Epilobium spp., 156
Epipactis helleborine, 172
Equisetum spp., 190

INDEX

Erigeron spp., 161
Eriophorum viridi-carinatum, 178
Erysimum cheiranthoides, 132
Erythronium spp., 127
Euonymus spp., 82, 195
Eupatorium maculatum, 159
     perfoliatum, 122
     purpureum, 159
     rugosum, 123
Euphorbia cyparissius, 136, 195
Evening Primrose, 137
Everlasting, Pearly, 125

Fagopyrum esculentum, 102
Fagus grandifolia, 39
False Solomon's Seal, 100, 195
     Starry, 100, 195
Fern, Bracken, 192
     Evergreen Wood, 192
     Lady, 192
     Marginal Wood, 192
     Ostrich, 192
     Rattlesnake, 190
     Sensitive, 192
     Spinulose Wood, 192
     Sweet-, 67
Fir, Balsam, 26
Fireweed, 156
Flag, Blue, 162
Fleabane, Daisy, 161
     Philadelphia, 161
     Rough Daisy, 161
Foamflower, 110
Forget-me-not, 165
     European, 165
Foxtail, Green, 180
Fragaria spp., 111
Fraxinus spp., 52, 53

Gale, Sweet, 67
Galium spp., 122
Garlic Mustard, 108
Gaultheria procumbens, 118
Gaylussacia baccata, 84
Gentians, 164
Gentiana andrewsii, 164
Gentianella crinita, 164
Geranium, Bicknell's, 154

Geranium (cont'd)
     Wild, 154
Geranium spp., 154
Gerardia, Purple, 158
     Slender, 158
Gerardia spp., 158
Geum aleppicum, 134
Ginger, Wild, 147
Ginseng, 176
     Dwarf, 176
Gleditsia triacanthos, 54
Goat's-beard, Yellow, 144
Goldenrod, Blue-stemmed, 139
     Canada, 139
     Early, 140
     Grass-leaved, 140
     Grey, 141
     Hairy, 123
     Rough-stemmed, 141
     Zigzag, 140
Goldthread, 105
Gooseberries, 71
Goosefoot, 174
Grape, Riverbank, 97
Grass, Annual Blue-, 180
     Common Blue-eyed, 163
     Cotton, 178
     Green Foxtail, 180
     Kentucky Blue-, 180
     Orchard, 180
     Quack, 180
     Rye, 180
     Slender Blue-eyed, 163
     Tape, 185
Grass of Parnassus, 111
Grass Pink, 151
Green Dragon, 186, 195
Greenbrier, Bristly, 96
Ground Cedar, 190
Ground Nut, 98, 194
Ground Pine, 190
Groundsel, Common, 144
Guelder Rose, 89
Gum, Black, 47
Gymnocladus dioica, 54

Hackberries, 43
Hamamelis virginiana, 59

Hawkweed, Mouse-ear, 145
      Orange, 146
      Yellow, 145
Hawthorns, 63
Hazelnut, American, 68
      Beaked, 68
Hazel, Witch-, 59
Heal-all, 167
Helianthus spp., 142
Helleborine, 172
Hemerocallis fulva, 145
Hemlock, Bulb-bearing Water, 115
      Eastern, 26
      Poison, 114, 195
      Water, 115, 195
Hemp, 172
      Indian, 156
Hepatica, Acute lobed, 106
      Round-lobed, 106
Hepatica spp., 106
Heracleum spp., 115, 195
Herb Robert, 154
Hesperis matronalis, 109
Hickories, 36
Hieracium spp., 145, 146
Hobble, Witch, 89
Hobblebush, 89
Hog Peanut, 98
Holly, Mountain-, 79, 195
Honeysuckle, Bracted, 93
      Bush, 92
      Fly, 93
      Hairy, 93
      Mountain Fly, 93
      Swamp Fly, 93
      Tartarian, 93
      Wild, 93
Hop-hornbeam, 38
Hop Tree, 72
Horehound, Cut-leaved Water-, 120
Horsetails, 190
Horseweed, 124
Huckleberry, Black, 84
Hypericum perforatum, 136
      virginicum, 150
Hydrophyllum spp., 119

Ilex verticillata, 79, 195

Impatiens spp., 146
Indian Cucumber-root, 128
Indian Hemp, 156
Indian Paint-brush, 149
Indian Pipe, 187
Indian Tobacco, 168
Inula helenium, 141
Iris, Dwarf Lake, 162
      Yellow, 162
Iris, spp., 162
Ironwood, 38
Ivy, Poison, 94, 195

Jack-in-the-pulpit, 186, 195
Jeffersonia diphylla, 107
Jerusalem Artichoke, 142
Jewel-weed, 146, 187, 194
      Pale, 146
      Pink, 146
Joe-Pye-weed, Green-stemmed, 159
      Spotted, 159
Juglans spp., 35
Juneberry, 62
Juniper, Common, 25
      Creeping, 25
Juniperus spp., 25

Kalmia spp., 87
Knotweed, Japanese, 152
      Prostrate, 102

Labrador Tea, 86
Lace, Queen Anne's, 116, 194
Lactuca spp., 171, 194
Ladies' -tresses, Nodding, 101
Lady Fern, 192
Lady's-slipper, Queen, 151
      Stemless, 151
      Yellow, 128
Lady's-thumb, 152
Lambkill, 87
Lamb's Quarters, 174
Laportea canadensis, 173
Larix laricina, 27
Lathyrus spp., 153
Laurel, Bog-, 87
      Sheep-, 87
Leather-leaf, 86

INDEX

Leatherwood, 82
Ledum groenlandicum, 86
Leek, Wild, 99
Lemna spp., 184
Leonurus cardiaca, 157
Lepidium spp., 108
Lettuce, Prickly, 171
    Tall White, 126
    White, 126
    Wild Blue, 171, 194
    Wild Canada, 171
Liatris spp., 159
Ligustrum vulgare, 78, 195
Lilac, Common, 78
Lilium philadelphicum, 146
Lily, Bluebead-, 127, 195
    Fragrant Water-, 105
    Orange Day-, 145, 194
    Trout, 127
    White Trout, 127
    Wood, 146
Linaria vulgaris, 138
Lindera benzoin, 69
Linnaea borealis, 158
Liriodendron tulipifera, 47
Lithospermum caroliniense, 147
Lobelia, Great, 169
    Kalm's, 169
Lobelia cardinalis, 149
    inflata, 168
    kalmii, 169
    siphilitica, 169
Locust, Black, 54, 195
    Honey, 54
Lolium perenne, 180
Lonicera spp., 92, 93
Loosestrife, Fringed, 137
    Prairie, 137
    Purple, 155
    Yellow, 137
Lotus corniculatus, 135
Lychnis alba, 104
Lycopodium spp., 190
Lycopus spp., 120
Lysimachia spp., 137
Lythrum salicaria, 155

Maclura pomifera, 46
Magnolia acuminata, 47

Maianthemum canadense, 100, 195
Mallow, Common, 155
    Musk, 155
Malus pumila, 43
Malva spp., 155
Maple, Ash-leaved, 51
    Black, 50
    Manitoba, 51
    Mountain, 64
    Red, 51
    Rock, 50
    Silver, 51
    Striped, 64
    Sugar, 50
Marigold, Bur-, 142
    Marsh, 129, 195
Marijuana, 172
Marsh Marigold, 129, 195
Matricaria matricarioides, 143
Matteuccia struthiopteris, 192
May-apple, 107, 195
Mayflower, 161
    Canada, 100
Mayweed, 126
Meadow-rue, Early, 175
    Purple, 175
    Tall, 175
Meadowsweet, Broad-leaved, 73
    Narrow-leaved, 73
Medeola virginiana, 128
Medicago lupulina, 135
    sativa, 162, 194
Medick, Black, 135
Melilotus alba, 112
    officinalis, 135
Menispermum canadense, 96, 195
Mentha arvensis, 167
Menyanthes trifoliata, 119
Mertensia spp., 165
Milfoil, Pale Water-, 185
Milkweed, Common, 157
    Swamp, 157
Mimulus ringens, 167
Mint, Field, 167, 194
Mitchella repens, 121
Mitella, spp., 111
Mitrewort, 111
    Naked, 111
Moccasin Flower, 151

Monarda ssp., 157
Moneses uniflora, 116
Monkey-flower, 167
Monotropa uniflora, 187
Moonseed, Canada, 96, 195
Moosewood, 64
Morus spp., 46, 194
Motherwort, 157
Mountain-ash, American, 60
           European, 60
           Showy, 60
Mountain-holly, 79, 195
Mouse-ear Chickweed, Common, 103
Mulberry, Red, 46, 194
       White, 46
Mullein, Common, 138, 194
Mustard, Black, 132
      Garlic, 108
      Hedge, 131
      Indian, 132
      Tumble, 131
      Wild, 132, 194
      Wórmseed, 132
Myosotis spp., 165
Myrica spp., 67
Myriophyllum spicatum
  var. *exalbescens,* 185

Nannyberry, 55
Nemopanthus mucronata, 79, 195
Nepeta cataria, 166, 194
Nettle, False, 173
    Stinging, 173, 194
    Wood-, 173
New Jersey Tea, 82
          Narrow-leaved, 82
Nightshade, Bittersweet, 98, 195
       Black, 98
       Enchanter's, 113
       Northern Enchanter's, 113
Ninebark, 72
Nut, Ground, 98
Nuphar variegatum, 129
Nyssa sylvatica, 47
Nymphaea spp., 105

Oak, Black, 42
    Bur, 40
    Chinquapin, 41

Oak (cont'd)
    Chestnut, 41
    Pin, 42
    Red, 41
    Swamp White, 41
    White, 40
Oats, Wild, 127
Oenothera biennis, 137
Onoclea sensibilis, 192
Orange, Osage, 46
Orchid, Tall Northern Green, 172
Orthilia secunda, 116
Osage Orange, 46
Osmorhiza claytoni, 114
Ostrya virginiana, 38
Oxalis europaea, 136
     montana, 117
     stricta, 136
Ox-eye Daisy, 126

Pagoda Tree, 65
Paint-brush, Indian, 149
Painted-cup, Scarlet, 149
Panax spp., 176
Parnassia glauca, 111
Parnassus, Grass of, 111
Parsnip, Cow, 115, 195
       Water, 115
Parthenocissus spp., 95
Partridgeberry, 121
Pawpaw, 58
Pea, Beach, 153
Pea Tree, 78
Peanut, Hog, 98
Pearly Everlasting, 125
Pedicularis spp., 138
Penstemon hirsuta, 158
Peppergrass, 108
      Field, 108
Pepperwort, 109
Phleum pratense, 180
Phlox, Wild Blue, 164
Phlox divaricata, 164
Physocarpus opulifolius, 72
Phytolacca americana, 122, 195
Picea spp., 30
Pickerel Weed, 162
Pigweed, 174, 194
     Redroot, 175, 194

INDEX

Pine, Eastern White, 28
    Ground, 190
    Jack, 28
    Pitch, 28
    Red, 28
    Scots, 28
Pineapple-weed, 143
Pink, Deptford, 148
    Grass, 151
Pinus spp., 28
Pipe, Indian, 187
Pipsissewa, 117
Pitcher-plant, 148
Plantago spp., 121, 194
Plantain, Common, 121, 194
    Pale, 121
    Water, 99
Platanthera hyperborea, 172
Platanus occidentalis, 48
Plum, Canada, 61
Poa spp., 180
Podophyllum peltatum, 107, 195
Pogonia ophioglossoides, 151
Pogonia, Rose, 151
Poison Hemlock, 114, 195
Poison Ivy, 94, 195
Pokeweed, 122, 194, 195
Polygala, Fringed, 154
Polygala pauciflora, 154
Polygonatum pubescens, 128, 195
Polygonum aviculare, 102
        coccineum, 152
        convolvulus, 102
        cuspidatum, 152
        lapathifolium, 152
        natans, 152
        persicaria, 152
Pondweed, Grassy, 185
Pontederia cordata, 162
Poplar, Balsam, 32
    White, 32
Populus spp., 32
Portulaca oleracea, 129, 194
Potamogeton gramineus, 185
Potentilla anserina, 133
    fruticosa, 92
    norvegica, 133
    palustris, 149
    recta, 133

Prenanthes spp., 126
Primrose, Bird's-eye, 156
    Evening, 137
Primula mistassinica, 156
Privet, Common, 78, 195
Prunella vulgaris, 167
Prunus spp., 49, 61, 195
Ptelea trifoliata, 72
Pteridium aqualinum, 192
Puccoon, 147
Purslane, 129, 194
Pussy-toes, Field, 125
    Plantain-leaved, 125
Pyrola, One-sided, 116
    Pink, 116
Pyrola spp., 116
Pyrus coronaria, 43

Queen Anne's Lace, 116, 194
Quercus spp., 40, 41, 42

Ragweed, Common, 176, 195
    Giant, 176
Ragwort, Balsam, 144
    Golden, 144
Raisin, Wild, 90
Ranunculus spp., 130
Raspberries, 76, 77
Rattlesnake Fern, 190
Redroot Pigweed, 175
Rhamnus spp., 66, 195
Rhus aromatica, 91, 195
    glabra, 58
    radicans, 94, 195
    typhina, 58
    vernix, 58
Ribes spp., 70-71
Ribgrass, 121
Robert, Herb, 154
Robinia pseudo-acacia, 54, 195
Rocket, Dame's, 109
    Wall, 131
Rosa spp., 74
Rose, Guelder, 89
    Pasture, 74
    Prickly Wild, 74
    Scotch, 74
    Smooth Wild, 74
    Swamp, 74

Rosemary, Bog-, 87
Rose Pogonia, 151
Rubus spp., 76, 77
Rudbeckia spp., 142
Rumex acetosella, 150
    crispus, 173, 194
Rushes, 178, 190
Rye, 180

Sagittaria latifolia, 99
St. John's-wort, Common, 136
       Marsh, 150
Salix spp., 34, 56
Salsify, 144
Salsola kali, 174
Sambucus spp., 91, 195
Sanguinaria canadensis, 107, 195
Sanicula marilandica, 114, 195
Saponaria officinalis, 104, 195
Sarracenia purpurea, 148
Sarsaparilla, Bristly, 113
      Wild, 113
Saskatoon, 62
Sassafrass, 48, 194
Sassafras albidum, 48
Saxifraga virginiensis, 110
Saxifrage, Early, 110
Scirpus americanus, 178
Scouring Rushes, 190
Scutellaria spp., 166
Sedges, 178
Sedum acre, 133
Self-heal, 167
Senecio spp., 144
Serviceberry, 62
Setaria viridis, 180
Shadbush, 62
Sheep-laurel, 87
Sheep-sorrel, 150
Shepherdia canadensis, 82
Shepherd's Purse, 109, 194
Shinleaf, 116
Sicyos angulatus, 97
Silene spp., 104
Silver-rod, 123
Silverweed, 133
Sinapsis arvensis, 132, 194
Sisymbrium spp., 131
Sisyrinchium spp., 163

Sium suave, 115
Skullcap, Common, 166
      Mad-dog, 166
Skunk Cabbage, 186, 195
Smartweed, Pale, 152
       Water, 152
Smilacina spp., 100, 195
Smilax spp., 96
Snakeroot, Black, 114
     White, 123, 195
Snowberry, 92
Soapberry, 83
Soapwort, 104, 195
Solanum spp., 98, 195
Solidago bicolor, 123
     caesia, 139
     canadensis, 139
     flexicaulis, 140
     graminifolia, 140
     hispida, 123
     juncea, 140
     nemoralis, 141
     rugosa, 141
Solomon's Seal, 128, 195
      Bog, 100
      False, 100, 195
      Starry False, 100, 195
Sonchus spp., 145, 194
Sorbus spp., 60
Sorrel, European Wood-, 117
     Sheep-, 117, 150
     Wood-, 117
     Yellow, 136
Sow-thistle, Common, 145, 194
     Field, 145
Sparganium eurycarpum, 182
Spatterdock, 129
Spearscale, 174, 194
Speedwell, Common, 168
Spicebush, 69
Spike-rush, 178
Spiraea spp., 73
Spiranthes cernua, 101
Spirodela polyrhiza, 184
Spring Beauty, Broad-leaved, 103
     Narrow-leaved, 103
Spring-cress, 152
Spruce, Black, 30
     Red, 30

INDEX

Spruce (cont'd)
    White, 30
Spurge, Cypress, 136, 195
Squashberry, 88
Squirrel Corn, 108, 195
Staphylea trifolia, 72
Star, Blazing, 159
Star-flower, 118
Steeplebush, 73
Stellaria media, 103, 194
Stinging Nettle, 173
Stonecrop, Mossy, 133
Strawberry, Barren, 134
    Common, 111
    Wood, 111
Strawberry-bush, Running, 82, 195
Streptopus roseus, 150, 195
Sumac, Fragrant, 91,195
    Poison, 58
    Smooth, 58
    Staghorn, 58
Sundews, 110
Sunflower, Woodland, 142
Susan, Black-eyed, 142
Swallow-wort, Black, 97
Swamp-betony, 138
Sweetbrier, 74
Sweet Cicely, 114
Sweet Clover, Yellow, 135
    White, 112
Sweet-fern, 67
Sweet Gale, 67
Sycamore, 48
Symphoricarpos spp., 92
Symplocarpus foetidus, 186, 195
Syringa vulgaris, 78

Tamarack, 27
Tapegrass, 185
Taraxacum spp., 144
Taxus canadensis, 25, 195
Tea, Labrador, 86
    Narrow-leaved New Jersey, 82
    New Jersey, 82
Teasel, 159
Thalictrum spp., 175
Thimbleberry, 76
Thimbleweed, 106
Thistle, Bull, 161

Thistle (cont'd)
    Canada, 160
    Common Sow-, 145, 194
    Field Sow-, 145
    Nodding, 160
    Russian, 174
    Swamp, 160
Thorn Apple, 120
Thuja occidentalis, 27
Tiarella cordifolia, 110
Tick-trefoil, 153
Tilia americana, 38
Timothy, 180
Toadflax, 138
    Bastard, 117
Tobacco, Indian, 168
Toothwort, 109
    Cut-leaved, 109
Touch-me-not, 146
Tragopogon spp., 144
Trailing Arbutus, 161
Tree of Heaven, 49
Trefoil, Bird's-foot, 135
    Tick-, 153
Trientalis borealis, 118
Trifolium hybridum, 153
    pratense, 153
    repens, 112
Trillium, Nodding, 101
    Painted, 101
    Red, 147
    White, 101
Trillium cernuum, 101
    erectum, 147
    grandiflorum, 101
    undulatum, 101
Triptoe, 89
Trout Lily, 127
    White, 127
Tsuga canadensis, 26
Tulip Tree, 47
Turtlehead, 121
Tussilago farfara, 143
Twinflower, 158
Twinleaf, 107
Twisted-stalk, Rose, 150, 195
Typha spp., 182, 194

Ulmus spp., 44

Urtica dioica, 173, 194
Utricularia spp., 139
Uvularia spp., 127

Vaccinium spp., 84, 85
Vallisneria americana, 185
Velvet-leaf, 155
Verbascum thapsus, 138, 194
Verbena hastata, 166
     urticifolia, 120
Veronica spp., 168
Vervain, Blue, 166
     White, 120
Vetch, Tufted, 163
Vetchling, 153
Viburnum, Maple-leaved, 88
     Snowball, 89
Viburnum acerifolium, 88
     alnifolium, 89
     cassinoides, 90
     dentatum, 90
     edule, 88
     lantana, 89
     lentago, 55
     opulus, 89
     rafinesquianum, 90
Vicia cracca, 163
Vincetoxicum medium, 97
Viola adunca, 163
     blanda, 112
     canadensis, 112
     conspersa, 163
     pallens, 112
     pubescens, 137
     rostrata, 163
Violet, Canada, 112
     Dog, 163
     Dog-tooth, 127
     Downy Yellow, 137
     Hooked-spur, 163
     Long-spurred, 163
     Northern White, 112
     Sweet White, 112
Viper's Bugloss, 165
Virginia Creeper, 95
Virginia Waterleaf, 119
Virgin's Bower, 95
Vitis riparia, 97

Waldsteinia fragarioides, 134

Wall Rocket, 131
Walnut, Black, 35
Water-flaxseed, 184
Water Hemlock, 115
     Bulb-bearing, 115
Water-horehound, 120
     Cut-leaved, 120
     European, 120
Waterleaf, Broad-leaved, 119
     Virginia, 119
Water-lily, Fragrant, 105
Watermeal, 184
Water-milfoil, Pale, 185
Water Parsnip, 115
Water Plantain, 99
Waterweed, Common, 184
Weed, Pickerel, 162
     Pineapple-, 143
Wild Asparagus, 102, 194
Wild Bergamot, 157
Wild Calla, 186, 195
Wild Carrot, 116, 194
Wild Columbine, 148
Wild Cucumber, 97
Wild Geranium, 154
Wild Ginger, 147
Wild Leek, 99
Wild Oats, 127
Wild Raisin, 90
Wild Sarsaparilla, 113
Willows, 34, 56
Willow Herb, Hairy, 156
Winterberry, 79, 195
Winter Cress, 132, 194
Wintergreen, 118, 194
     One-flowered, 116
Witch-hazel, 59
Witch Hobble, 89
Wolf Berry, 92
Wolffia spp., 184
Wood-betony, 138
Wood Lily, 146
Wood-sorrel, 117
     European, 117

Yarrow, 125, 194
Yew, American, 25, 195

Zanthoxylum americanum, 69

GLOSSARY

achene – a small dry 1-seeded fruit (typical of asters)

annual – lasting for 1 year only

basal – at the base of the plant

berry – a fleshy fruit formed from a single ovary and containing several seeds

biennial – a plant that lives for 2 years and blooms in the second

bract – a small modified leaf often beneath a flower or in an inflorescence

capsule – a dry fruit formed from a compound ovary (of more than 1 carpel) that opens along 1 or more lines when mature

carpel – one of the units of a compound ovary; a simple ovary has 1 carpel

catkin – dry scaly spike of either male or female flowers (e.g. as in willows)

clasping – often refers to leaves when they partly surround the stem

cordate – heart-shaped; refers to overall leaf shape or leaf base

entire – leaf margins without teeth

floret – a small flower, usually one of a dense cluster or head (e.g. as in grasses or Asters)

follicle – a dry fruit formed from a simple ovary which splits along 1 side

gland – a secretory structure

inflorescence – the complete flower cluster including axis and bracts

involucre – the circle of bracts around a flower cluster or head

introduced – brought relatively recently from another region

obovate – egg-shaped, with the broadest end near the tip

ovate – egg-shaped, with the broadest end near the base

pappus – the bristles (modified calyx) forming a crown on top of each achene in the asters

perennial – living for more than 2 years

pith – the softer, central part of a twig or stem

rachis – the axis of an inflorescence or compound leaf

receptacle – the portion of an axis bearing the organs of a flower or the collected flowers of an Aster family head

rhizome – an underground stem usually growing horizontally and rooting at the nodes

rosette – a cluster of leaves crowded together at the base of a plant

rugose – wrinkled; usually describing the surface of a leaf or seed

sessile – stalkless, e.g. leaf blade attached directly to the stem without petiole

sheath – a tubular envelope around the stem (e.g. as in grasses)

sinus – the recess between 2 lobes of a leaf

smooth – without roughness; also used here to describe the condition when no hairs are present

spathe – a large bract enclosing a group of flowers

sp. – species; a basic category in plant classification

spp. – two or more species

ssp. – subspecies; a subdivision of plants within a species

spur – a hollow sac-like or tubular extension of a sepal or petal in a flower

stipule – the appendage at the base of a leaf or leaf stalk

tuber – an enlarged portion of an underground stem, mainly used for food storage

var. – variety; a distinct group of variants within a species

woolly – with curled hairs which may be tangled together